Dorset
Voices

Pier Theatre, Bournemouth – Mike Smithwick

Dorset Voices

A collection of new prose, poetry and photographs

Roving
Press

Edited and compiled by Poundbury Voices
Compilation © Roving Press 2012
Individual work © 2012 The Contributors

Published by Roving Press Ltd
4 Southover Cottages, Frampton, Dorset, DT2 9NQ, UK
Tel: +44 (0)1300 321531
www.rovingpress.co.uk

First published 2012 by Roving Press Ltd

ISBN: 978-1-906651-15-2

British Library Cataloguing in Publication Data
A catalogue record for this book is available from the British Library

Front cover image: Behind the front, Bournemouth, by Jessica Knight
Back cover main image: Strolling exhibit, The Cobb, Lyme Regis, by Mike
Smithwick

Set in 11.5/13 pt Minion by Beamreach (www.beamreachuk.co.uk)
Printed and bound in England by Hentry Ling Ltd, at the Dorset Press,
Dorchester, DT1 1HD.

Contents

Foreword by HRH The Prince of Wales   *vii*
Preface   *viii*
Acknowledgements   *xi*

The Writers

Robin Daglish	The view from Poundbury	1
Antonia Nevill	Dorset, with love	2
Lilian Irene Thomas	'Treasures' – days and ways	4
Jennifer Grierson	Swanage revisited	9
Julian Nangle	A day at Chydyok	13
Lucy Nankivell	Chesil Beach to New Forest	14
Geraldine Farrow	Swannery	16
Jennifer Stewkesbury	A Portland life	18
Benjamin Blech	The world has changed; so must Dorset	22
Claire Wyburn	Wedding dress	27
Paddy Hughes	High Dorset	32
Janet Hancock	Memory	33
Andy Case	Shepherd's warning	36
Andy Case	September love	36
Timmy Crump	Odd encounter in Shaftesbury	37
Pam Kelly	Susan Henchard, Dorchester Fair, 1886	38
Lesley Burt	In the priory graveyard	39
Frederick Rea Alexander	Never forget	40
Frederick Rea Alexander	Burnt	40
Helen Pizzey	Nautical map	41
Valerie Bridge	'Where are you to?'	42
Nigel Palfrey	Forgotten uses of furze	44
Judy Bannon	The bridge	48
Megan Cannon	Fitz's story	51
Frances Colville	On a Dorset cliff-top	55
Maya Pieris	Battered fish	56
Janet Gogerty	Four days in June	57
Jeanette Lowe	Too loved to say goodbye	63
Gail Aldwin	Dusting off the memories	69
Phil Mullane	Liberation song 2001	70
Patrick O'Neill	The box	71
Karen Wright	The landslip	77
Audrey Lee	Lady Caroline Pountney	78
Margery Hookings	The world from my window	81
Judy Hall	Circle song	84

Bronwen Coe	'Dead slow'	88
Jim Aldhouse	Isar Defoe	90
Janet Wadsworth	The cottage	93
Anne Clegg	Exploring our Jurassic Coast	97

The Photographers

Mike Smithwick	Pier Theatre, Bournemouth	ii
Maya Pieris	Tide lines, West Bay	xii
Janet Wells	Seagulls at sunset, Rawtock Pier, Poole	3
Caitlin Palmer	Jetty reflection, The Fleet	7
Doff Davies	Boogie woogie duet, Sturminster Newton festival	8
Laura Gardner	Bridport market	12
Merete Bates	February dawn	15
Laura Edwards	Portland Bill	17
Scott Irvine	St Andrew's graveyard and Rufus Castle, Portland	21
Maria Konstanse Bruun	Walking the dogs in Bournemouth	26
Scott Irvine	St George's Church, Portland	31
Katie Stenhouse	Abandoned	35
Emma Foot	Lone tree	37
Rosy Emberley	Ringstead Beach reflections	39
Alicia Chambers-Hill	Bees	43
Bronwen Coe	Moses saving the Israelites, St Basil's Church, Toller Fratrum	50
Rosanna Wilmott	Poppies	54
Sarah Gilpin	Low tide at Portland Bill	62
Jessica Knight	'Up is down' river reflection, Blandford	68
Sarah Gilpin	Flaky Portland rock	76
Abbie Williams	Hive Beach	80
Bronwen Coe	In the summerhouse shadows	87
Becky Hinsley	Mortain Bridge, Blandford	89
Joff Rees	Anne-Marie Vincent	96

| **Writers' Biographies** | | **98** |
| **Poundbury Voices – Editors' Biographies** | | **103** |

Louisa Adjoa Parker	This lonely night	105
Maria Strani-Potts	Rehearsing 'I do'	109
Jim Potts	The Gap	111

| **Useful Contacts** | | **114** |
| **Publisher's Note** | | **116** |

Foreword

by HRH The Prince of Wales

CLARENCE HOUSE

Building a community is a much more complex process than you would think. My contribution to Poundbury, through the Duchy of Cornwall, has been the land, the planning and the bricks and mortar. It is the residents attracted to live there who have made it what it is today. It proves to me that building carefully can enhance human potential and, perhaps, contribute to social cohesion as well, just as the opposite can do so much harm.

I am delighted, therefore, that some of the residents of Poundbury have come together to share a love of poetry, reminiscences and stories – as they say, everyone has a story to tell – and have compiled such a splendid anthology. I pray it will give pleasure and inspiration to others.

Preface

As Poundbury matures and develops its distinctive identity, it offers a new perspective on Dorset and the surrounding towns and countryside. Just as the whole of Dorset influences the people of Poundbury, so too does Poundbury have the potential to become a new creative hub and source of inspiration for the people of Dorset and further afield. Poundbury is a mixed community and is proud of its social diversity and atmosphere of social inclusion. We are all incomers here, with diverse origins.

HRH The Prince of Wales had a vision of an environment notable for its new urban planning, its architectural styles and the traditional crafts, skills and materials used to create this impressive extension of the county town of Dorchester. 'I am very keen to try something different', he wrote in *A Vision of Britain* (1989), acknowledging that 'the participation of the people of Dorchester is needed', and expressing the belief that 'vision and boldness are also needed if we are to produce something of real beauty in the English countryside'.

It goes without saying that the three editors of *Dorset Voices*, all residents of Poundbury, share that vision, but they also want to supplement the built environment with a new spirit of intergenerational creativity that embraces literature and the Arts, including photography. There are critics who do not appreciate the mixture of architectural styles, vernacular and neoclassical, traditional and modern. This anthology of Dorset writing also presents a mixture, from the humorous dialect poem to classical short stories and cutting-edge prose.

We shouldn't forget that William Barnes modelled many of his Dorset dialect poems on foreign verse forms, thanks to his scholarly knowledge of other literary cultures. Thomas Hardy was very aware of Ancient Greek tragedy and the history of Roman Dorchester. We venture to suggest that he would have found Poundbury a fitting extension of Casterbridge. Stone-inscribed quotations from poems of both Barnes (*Woone Rule*: 'What is, is best, we needen fear') and Hardy (*Nature's Questioning*: 'Life and Death are neighbours nigh') can be contemplated at Poundbury Cemetery. Both writers have remained a powerful source of inspiration for Dorset people, and many of the submissions we received reflected their enduring influence.

Poundbury's proximity to Maiden Castle and Poundbury Camp provides a powerful historical context and feeling of cultural continuity to its fortunate residents, and it is not easy to forget that it is watched over by the remains of a Romano-Celtic Temple, dedicated perhaps to the goddess Minerva. In his poem *The view from Poundbury* (included in this collection), Robin

Daglish writes of passing Dorchester people feeling the weight of bones under grass:

I can almost hear the whispering below ...
On long winter nights the stories would be told,
round crackling campfires they would poke
the logs and read their dreams in smoke ...

Poundbury was the initial inspiration for this anthology and that is why the editorial team is called *Poundbury Voices*. But the anthology represents writing from all over Dorset, as befits a new developing community that both feels an integral part of the county town and aspires to become a creative hub for the whole of the county.

Poundbury/Dorchester as a whole is well situated to become such a hub; it acts as a magnet and draws people in from the surrounding districts, but residents are also fortunate to have immediate access to all of Dorset's areas of outstanding natural beauty, its delightful villages and the Jurassic Coast.

The publication of the *Dorset Voices* anthology takes place in the year of the Cultural Olympiad, and the year when Poundbury's Queen Mother Square promises to become the centrepiece of this exciting new urban development and, who knows, the key destination of a new coffee-house artistic and literary culture. Let's make it the Dorset equivalent of Prague's Wenceslas Square!

Dorset Voices draws on the literary and photographic talents of the people of Dorset. The editors' aim was to create a book full of images and quality writing of real beauty and interest, with the photographs adding to the appeal of the book but not connected with the individual contributions of text. We are delighted to have received a portfolio of outstanding photographs submitted by students at the excellent Thomas Hardye School, another magnet for families all over the county. Not surprisingly, Ofsted inspectors rated it as one of the best comprehensive schools in the country.

Our starting-point was the firm belief that everyone here has a story to tell. We believe that there are many talented writers and photographers (both established and unpublished) in our communities, who deserve to have their work made available for the appreciation of others.

Maria Strani-Potts
Louisa Adjoa Parker
Jim Potts, OBE

Poundbury fountain

Acknowledgements

The editors of *Dorset Voices* would like to thank Julie and Tim Musk of Roving Press, a small Dorset publishing house with an impressive list of titles. They shared our vision. We would also like to thank HRH The Prince of Wales, Simon Conibear, Estate Director, Dorchester, for the Duchy of Cornwall, and Dominic Tambling of Creative Dorset, as well as all the contributors and everyone who sent in their submissions. We are only sorry that space did not allow the inclusion of more submissions, many of which were excellent. The final selection was made on the principle that all three members of the editorial team had to cast a firm vote of support for each piece to be included. Thank you all for participating and for sharing your work with us.

Tide lines, West Bay – Maya Pieris

The view from Poundbury
Robin Daglish

They were nearly houses with not-quite-bathrooms
and almost-halls. They were shavings, scaffolding
and almost-walls. They were ribs of rafters waiting
for their nails, felt and batten ready for their tiles.

Beyond the by-pass Maiden Castle shoulders the skies,
snow falls in silence, sheeting the fields;
I can almost hear the whispering below.
The candle of the sun lights this amnesia of snow:
the purity of a fresh start when the trail is cold.

On long winter nights the stories would be told,
round crackling campfires they would poke
the logs and read their dreams in smoke,
all our yesterdays encoded in cloud: the coma
of centuries scrolling over.

When hailstones clatter you can almost hear
the splinter and give before the battering ram,
wooden gates bursting like a dam:
sword and spear, death and fear.
And now as leisurely Dorchester people pass,
you can almost feel the weight of bones under grass.

Dorset, with love

Antonia Nevill

So, you want the perfect marriage of sea, coastline and countryside – simple! Come to the south-west region of Dorset, a county I had scarcely heard of before I fell passionately in love with it over 50 years ago. There is no place on earth where I would rather live. Don't expect high drama; nothing is vast or flamboyant; you won't be overwhelmed, intimidated or humbled, but welcomed, embraced, enfolded and soothed into a tranquil pace of life. Just for a moment, put aside any preconceptions, ignore the 'hype' and the tourist brochures and open up your own five senses; give them free rein and allow them to be your guide and mentor.

Let your eyes absorb the ever-changing colours and moods of the broad expanse of sea, now Mediterranean blue, now gunmetal, now slashed with white rollers or so pale it merges with the horizon. It is the setting for vessels of all shapes and sizes – sailing boats large and small, fishing trawlers, immense cargo ships. Look at the golden sands of beautiful Weymouth Bay (the 'Naples of England'). Let your gaze take in the strange craggy isle of Portland, sweep across Lyme Bay along the pebbled miles of unique Chesil Bank, past the centuries-old swannery at Abbotsbury, and the towering vertiginous cliff of Golden Cap, before alighting on snug Lyme Regis.

Turn your eyes inland to rest gratefully on the green, rolling, rounded hills, the darker green of woods, the broad valleys in between, where honey-coloured stone villages and graceful manor houses – but no hint of chocolate box – nestle amid a patchwork of hedged fields and meadows, and where rivers, barely more than streams, meander unhurriedly past crops or flocks of sheep or sleek dairy cattle. Be dazzled by the brilliant gold of rape, entranced by the occasional ephemeral blue lake of flax, gladdened by the wealth of wild flowers – no matter if you can't name them. Enjoy the pleasure of spotting a multitude of wild birds and animals.

Next, let your urban-deadened ears revel in the total silence of the open heath, then catch the murmur of ripples on shingle, or the roar of fiercer waves crashing against rocks; the calls of gulls, or that skylark ascending – yet again – and the constant low hum of bees and insects in the heather.

Fill your lungs with air straight from the Atlantic, so pure it almost hurts, perhaps carrying a hint of seaweed or the tang of freshly caught fish just landed at Weymouth, Bridport or Lyme, or sniff the almond-like scent of gorse bloom, sweet new-mown hay, or wild garlic in the hedgerows. Culinary delicacies abound. Let loose your taste buds on local seafood, cheeses, cider, honey, cream, apple-cake, to be savoured in some comfortable old pub, where the soft burr of Dorset voices drifts, as it has for centuries, up to the ancient smoke-blackened beams.

Feel the exhilarating tingle of the sea, the softness of the sand between your toes, the springiness of the turf as you walk over the green hills, the sun on your face, a gentle west wind stirring your hair. Or perhaps you prefer the challenge of braving wilder elements, as a fiercer wind buffets you and sends salt spray to shower you? Above all, feel your entire being relax and adapt to the spirit and essence of the place.

Now your imagination can have its turn. Let it run riot and picture the time when this region was home to the amazing creatures whose myriad fossils testify to their existence here. People this glorious landscape with characters from its past, real or fictitious: woad-smeared ancestors manning the Iron Age forts; Roman soldiers; Saxon and Norman invaders; medieval monks in their monasteries; Roundheads and Cavaliers; Judge Jeffreys; Mary Anning; John Fowles; the Mayor of Casterbridge and Hardy's dramatic heroines, Tess and Bathsheba, all against the backdrop of villages whose whimsical names so delighted John Betjeman.

Whatever your interests, spanning the alphabet from architecture to zoology, via botany, fishing, golf, fossil-hunting, geology, kite-surfing, ornithology, sailing, hiking, swimming, extreme sports – you name it – Dorset can offer bountiful material, from a simple 'taster' to a lifelong pursuit. Do I exaggerate? Don't take my word for it, come and judge for yourself.

Seagulls at sunset, Rawtock Pier, Poole – Janet Wells

'Treasures' – days and ways

Lilian Irene Thomas

Casting my mind back over almost 86 years, to when I was born in the medieval market town of Sturminster Newton in Dorset, I know what a heritage is ours – to roam free in fields and woods, to cycle the beautiful country lanes, or to reach all the delightful areas of our county by road or rail.

I lived with my father, a Bespoke Tailor and Outfitter, my mother, two brothers and a sister. We lived 'over the shop' as they say. The premises overlooked the marketplace, where from the large upper window we had a good view of general activities. On Boxing Day we watched the local Hunt gather for the traditional Stirrup Cup, before setting off with horses and hounds – a real country life scene.

During the War years when regiments of troops used our town for manoeuvres, we watched the huge Centurion tanks negotiate, with great dexterity, the narrow streets without any damage whatsoever to adjacent buildings. The fields by the River Stour became muddy – almost to the point of wiping out the lush green grass. We watched the building of Bailey bridges across the river. Too young to go to the War, I, along with other girls in the Girl's Training Corps, were engaged in making camouflaged netting. The nets were strung from the ceiling in a large upper room, taken over from the local Methodist Church. Here we wove, in and out, strips of canvas webbing – green, orange and fawn. We also collected for the Red Cross – selling draw tickets in aid of food parcels for the troops.

I find myself bypassing the early years of our childhood days – these cannot be overlooked! We went to the local schools where we had dedicated teachers, who gave us a good sound education, with all the basic things we would need as we grew to adulthood. They also trained us to be good citizens, with a respect for our county and for King and country. At the Junior School, now called William Barnes, we had our bottle of milk at playtime and ate the two biscuits which were carefully wrapped by our mother. An elderly gentleman, a retired schoolmaster who came to stay at a house next to the school, would throw pennies into the playground, and enjoyed watching the children scrabble for them! We learnt to dance the Maypole and country dancing. At the Senior School we did acting, and performed later in the British Legion Hut, our then Village Hall. The Hut, as we called it, was used for all entertainments – film shows, dances and school plays. One year, our school did a mime for Christmas. I recall the smell of the greasepaint, and the terrific heat of the thick blue wool blanket, as I knelt on stage as the Virgin Mary.

To a truly born-and-bred country person, market day was a real delight – at least it was in our town! I can never forget the rumble of cattle lorries, dung dripping through the wooden slats and pink noses peeping out, as the cattle were driven down to the stalls and pens in the cattle section of the town, or the sight of stall holders busily setting out their wares in the marketplace.

On a market day, I doubt if much was absorbed in our brains at school! As soon as the bell rang at 12 noon, we raced home to let our parents know we were home. Rushing out again, with an agitated word from mother, 'Don't be late – you've not had your dinner' – and we were off to the cattle market. Here we went among the stalls and pens, the smell of dung everywhere. The cows slithered about as they pounded into the huge weighing machine, before entering the ring to be sold. Farmers prodded and poked the animals with their sticks as the auctioneer's voice droned on and on. We sat among the farmers, fascinated by the huge dial of the weighing machine, which looked like a huge clock. There was just time to see the hens, rabbits, puppies, sheep and pigs, before racing home, gobbling our dinner and back to school for 1.30 pm. Sometimes we went around the stalls in the marketplace instead, and we learnt so much from all we saw, such as the pulling and stretching of the toffee mixture over a bar before it was cut into humbug cushion shapes with special scissors. How often we raced indoors to beg our parents to buy stacks of boxes of Caley's chocolates going very cheaply around Christmas-time – but our parents never did buy, much to our disappointment.

When I was on holiday from school, father allowed me to serve the farmers who came into the shop. Here I gained knowledge of how to meet people and deal with customers, which I greatly enjoyed. Selling Panama hats – which then cost 3/6 in old money – as well as ties, socks, braces and hankies, to farmers or their wives. After school, on market days, the marketplace took on a deathly silence; a smell of rotting oranges, empty crates and rubbish filled the air. We children rummaged through it all, as there were treasures to find. Much of the fruit came wrapped in tissue paper; on each piece was a picture of the country of origin – and we were collectors! To find a new picture that we did not have was indeed a real treasure. As the rubbish was cleared away, our market day was over for another week, except for the mooing of the cattle, waiting to be collected from the station yard. When the disaster of Foot and Mouth struck the Fat Stock Market at Christmas one year, everyone was devastated. The slaughter of all the cattle was done, and the stench of burning hung on the air for over three weeks. The smell seeped into everything and everywhere. No one who loves animals can ever forget such a tragedy.

Our little town was steeped in old world charm. The sweet shop with its tinkling door bell, where we stood looking in the window at gob stoppers, sherbet dabs, liquorice laces and wheels, aniseed balls, humbugs, fruity chews, snowy bonbons and teacake sweets. The latter had a unique cherry flavour all of their own. Trying to decide on what to spend our half-penny pocket money needed time. In the doorway stood the figure of the owner, like a true Dickensian gentleman. He would wait patiently, one finger in a waistcoat pocket, his watch and chain in the other, to welcome customers into his little shop. The bakehouse, too, was a sheer delight; watching the dough being prepared and put into the large metal mixing drum. After a short wait, out it came to be kneaded into shapes and put into tins, then onto the long-handled tray-like shovel and into the hot oven, to come tumbling out baked and crusty. The baker would tap the base of each loaf with his knuckles to make sure it was cooked. In the window of the baker's shop were all the delights to choose from – doughnuts, iced buns, jam tarts and many more, lardy cake being the greatest favourite of all. Adjacent to the bakehouse was a shed storing the huge bags of flour, where the school friend who lived at the bakehouse and I would clamber over all these bags, coming out covered in flour and looking like snowmen.

At the top of the road where our Granny lived stood the blacksmith's forge. As you can guess, we visited Granny quite often, so that we could visit the forge. We would stand at the door and watch the blacksmith at work – the sparks flying upward from the fire as the metal was heated and shaped into horseshoes. The horses waited patiently as the horseshoe was nailed into place. We would look on in horror as the blacksmith hammered long nails into a horse's hoof. We were sure it hurt them, despite the smithy's words of reassurance that it did *not* hurt the horse at all. We hardly believed it, but there was no reaction from the horse, except perhaps an impatient stamp of the hoof as if it wanted to be off. The smell of singed horsehair would waft through the open door.

There was the saddler's shop with the lovely smell of leather coming out into the country air; harnesses and saddles hanging up for sale. The ironmonger's too, with its smell of oil and paraffin – how I loved the smell of these places! Down a pathway to the bank of the River Stour was the wheelwright's business. Here we watched them at work making the wheels for wagons and carts, hammering spokes of wood into circular wheel frames, heating the round metal rim, which was made a little larger to allow for the metal to shrink perfectly to the wheel. When in place, water was thrown over the metal rim to shrink it. How the size was judged so accurately to ensure a perfect fit was a skilled work of art. We truly learnt much from what we saw in those days.

Our River Stour held sad and happy memories too. Our father was always giving us warnings, 'Keep away from the river'. Do children always heed what parents say? We were no different to the others! When the floods were out, we waded in with water reaching the top of our wellies, not knowing where the edge of the field or the edge of the riverbank was. An old raft of wood was supported on empty petrol drums. This was tied to the bank. We would get on it and rock up and down, regardless of the danger, or the fact that none of us could swim! There were accidental drownings, even of strong swimmers, because of the danger of being sucked into the underwater waterlily growth. Uncle would take us in a rowing boat for picnics between the water mills situated along the banks. When the river is in flood, sluice gates are fully open, and to see the surge of water over the steps of a fall and between the bridges is quite spectacular. I used to sit on the old mill wall watching the pigeons flying in and out of their coots on the wall, imitating their calls so often that they are registered quite firmly in my brain. As I listen to those birds today, I notice a change, a note missing here and there. Someone's pigeon mum is not doing her job!

We had many memorable activities to brighten our days, like the flower shows, Vicarage fetes, fair days, along with other local activities of country life.

We never had a Christmas tree in our home, so one year we went onto the Common and tugged away at a gorse bush. Picking off the yellow flowers we went triumphantly home, weary and with heavily pricked fingers. That year we had a lovely Christmas tree. Another year the keeper of the woods gave me a conifer branch, after a walk of about four miles to collect it. We enjoyed the things we had to strive for and appreciated all we had. Sad though it may be, just as the pigeons have changed their call, changes come, as I guess they must. Our medieval market town has seen changes along with many others. As I look back, with the many memories stored in my mind, and the glow in my heart, I am glad I have had a share in the great heritage which is ours to possess.

I would like to feel that every Dorset-born child, on looking back as I have done, will feel that they too are in possession of a wonderful heritage, that of being born and bred in the County of Dorset!

Jetty reflection, The Fleet – Caitlin Palmer

Boogie woogie duet, Sturminster Newton festival – Doff Davies

Swanage revisited

Jennifer Grierson

Two long hours bumping and rattling in the Ring and Ride bring us here from Lyme. Fifty years since I've been here! Let out, I dodge between the cars, climb the grassy slope, and suddenly the whole of this sun-blessed, beautiful, generous bay spreads itself in front of me. It's all there, every bit of it! Just as it used to be, held safe in the arms of my beloved white cliffs. I let out a great sigh of relief, breathe in a fresh supply of sea air, and walk forward.

The smell is right – salty and sea-weedy – and my eyes immediately look down, checking for shells. Yes, they're here! I pick up a few, just as I used to, twists of silvery moon shells, fragments of shifting emerald-pink-purple, orange and yellow curled snail shells, treasures to keep safe. Dried scraps of seaweed, greens, pinks, browns, some soft, some crisp, lie on the fine, dense sand. Shoes off, to walk along in the edge of the sea, avoiding the stones which hurt my feet, like they did before.

The blue and white sky is reflected in the water, set dancing by the wind. Small, warm waves are gently rolling over my feet with quiet foaming noises up the shallow slope of the beach, leaving little snaking ridges as they slide back again. There are only a few people here, mostly little children being encouraged by their grandparents to skim stones. A child holds up her hand to me, silently expecting the shell I've just picked up, and I give it with a smile, glad to connect with her. Perhaps I did the same.

High above us glides a single seagull, the sun making the thin ends of its tail and wing feathers blaze a brilliant white. Ahead of me, where the town spills onto the promenade, I hear loud music playing and, nearer, I realise it's a jazz band. 'If you can't beat 'em, join 'em' comes to mind, so I gently dance my way along the water's edge, adding watery swishes to the beat. As I come to the sheltering curve of the sea wall, the water's a little colder, the waves quieter, and I want to stop awhile.

Here's the slipway reaching down to the sea. At its base there's a worn stone block set in the water and its seaweed cushion looks dry enough to sit on. Before I go any further, I want to write, now, at these shifting boundaries between sea and land, between memories and the here-and-now.

***

Swanage has been a special place to me ever since my early childhood. Every summer, we – my mother, father, younger brother and I – came here on the old paddle steamer from Bournemouth Pier for a special treat.

But, as in all the best adventures, there's an ordeal first; we have to pass along a narrow walkway at the side of the pier in order to board the boat. Here we are out of the sunshine and down in cold shadow; on one side men stand fishing, which I hate; it hurts me when they angrily kick the crabs back. On the other side there aren't any railings, only looping metal chains, and I fearfully watch the heavy slopping of dark green waves crashing into each other underneath the pier. To make it worse, I have to trust my feet to walk on nothing more than a metal lattice where I can see through the diamond-shaped holes to the water below. At any moment we might somehow slip through and drown just down there, between the barnacle-encrusted wooden piles which support the pier. As an adult I realise this was to let water-splashes drain away, but at the time it seemed I had to endure a test of bravery, and never said a word. But after that is pure joy – deciding which seats to bag on the breezy deck, hanging over the sides watching the dancing green-white water churned flying by the huge paddle wheels. Flinging specially saved crusts of bread sky-high for the swooping seagulls, visiting the noise-filled engine room to view men in overalls proudly wiping the gleaming brass piston rods with oily cloths, standing at the stern watching our wake endlessly disappearing as we travel past the unfolding white cliffs, so mysterious after our golden ones.

All this is forgotten as we arrive at Swanage Pier, with its nice, safe, swirly patterned iron wall-railings and wooden floorboards which make my sandals clack in a friendly way. It is a very long walk. My string bag, stuffed tight with swimming costume, towel, jersey, sunhat and sandwiches tucked safe inside my tin bucket, bumps and scratches my bare legs. I grip my wooden spade in my other hand, and my stomach's tight, high up in my chest. Now, at last, we can actually push our feet down into the sand's crunch; we are overcome by the beloved smell of drying seaweed, and the heat comes bouncing at us off the chalk cliffs. We are well and truly here. The journey from land, over-sea to this faraway shore, has worked its magic once again, and the long day is ours.

After swimming we eat, then walk along the cliff-top over to Durlston Head, and there we rest, looking down on the topsides of seagulls gliding over the silent, shining, wrinkled sea far below. It is these cliff-tops, with their wonderful spaciousness that, in the end, I love most of all. On my bedroom wall at home still hangs a treasured calendar I was given when I was five, which had a poem with each month's picture. And for *my* month, my birthday month of June, it said:

> Up on the cliffs, beside the sea.
> That's where Jennifer loves to be.

It was true, and has become even more so ever since. Later I came to understand that there'd been an even earlier feeding of this special cliff-top love, particularly white cliffs. It happened while I was in Kent, visiting the South Foreland Lighthouse near Dover, where my much-beloved great-grandfather had been the chief engineer in the late nineteenth century. Six of his children were born there, and my grandma and her seven brothers and sisters lived there for many years, all of them walking more than a mile along the cliff path to the little school in the village. Even my mother had stayed there, as a sort of refugee, when she was a child. All this was their home and life on the tall white cliffs: the charming Victorian lighthouse with its clutch of keepers' cottages, surrounded by nothing more than the green spread of turf and a great airiness, the French white cliffs across the narrow sea-straits, and far down below, the ships forever passing to and fro. A great love for this home was deeply embedded in the psyche of my family.

So I was standing there by the Lighthouse, thinking about them all, and gazing down, just as they did, at the passing ships, when I realised there was yet another ingredient in this love-mix of mine. In July of 1946, my mother, father, brother Michael and I were on board the *Carnaervon Castle* sailing from Capetown to Southampton, and so we ourselves had been on one of those ships passing the White Cliffs of Dover! This in itself would have been a poignant experience for us, and the many thousands more returning home to England, but for our family to be welcomed by our own family lighthouse – for my mother to be able to point it out to us all, to greet it, own it, claim it, *love it* – would have been even more moving and meaningful. A sense of special love for these landmarks, symbols of home, safety, belonging and happiness, would have been firmly planted in my hungry four-year-old spirit.

✳✳✳

So for me, on my own now, and an OAP, this day-trip back to Swanage is a joyful pilgrimage. No wonder I bolted off the bus on my own! I want to look closely, here at the end of the slipway, this Janus place. The water's very shallow here; there's just enough space for the seaweed to tickle my feet as it wafts over them. The breeze makes little waves, gently clumping the seaweeds into a textile, a knotted carpet – a jumble of lime, dark green, yellow, russet, gold, apricot, crimson, ginger, bronze. Some are delicate, like the sea-lettuce, others a rugged statement, like the bladderwrack. Then there are long brown strings lazily twisting like serpents over the ochre sand beneath. Some float, drifting slowly back and forth, others swoosh more vigorously, safely anchored to their home-rock.

A fly keeps crawling on my knee, and my feet are getting cold, but I haven't finished yet. A seagull shadow passes over my neck, onto the sand and then at a sharp angle up the high sea wall. The sea surface is dancing with reflections of blue sky and the soft-edged white clouds moving towards the horizon. The sea-line itself is indigo, changing to deep green turquoise, gently smudging to pale jade. A floating curved seagull feather sails in like a little boat, runs ashore and sticks, trembling in the breeze. The jazz music resumes, calling me. My feet are very cold, and I realise that the tide, disguised with warmth, has crept in and up around my skirt and sweater. Time to move on.

I eat my picnic near the jazz band, which has been joined by more and more musicians; it's the culmination of Jazz Week. Then I walk past the new pier and begin to climb up the headland. Here, on Peveril Point, I am in heaven again. High up, nothing but glorious space stretching out on all sides – the sky feels enormous, and I expand into it. Eastwards, past the far side of Swanage Bay, I can see Old Harry and the white cliffs beyond stretching their shining repeats away into the distance; behind that are the faint glimmerings of Bournemouth, and I feel the connection, all along the coastline, to Dover's far-off white cliffs.

I sit close to the edge amongst the wild flowers starring the warm turf and gaze down at the waves foaming their lace-dance a hundred feet below. The sunshine warms everything and makes all the different whites, blues and greens bright and beautiful. It shines green through the walls of the waves as they ride in, breathing out their peaceful meditation sound over and over again. I listen for a long time. The breeze blows my spirit; gives it the freedom to fly, to swoop, to glide and float out into the space.

Then I remember I have to go back for the bus, but first I stand there on the cliff edge, like a great angel with huge wings, giving forth lovings, blessings and thanksgivings. My heart sings *Amen, Amen, Amen.*

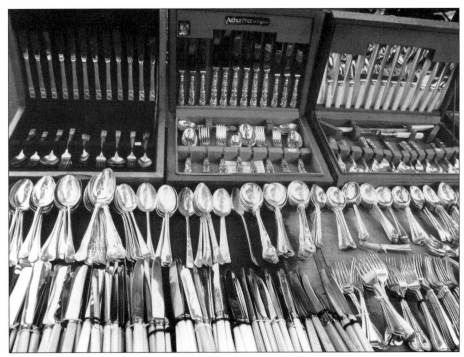

Bridport market – Laura Gardner

A day at Chydyok
Julian Nangle

(In memory of Llewelyn Powys)

How is it I am led
Unseen with your soft eyes, across the brush
Of countryside you championed with your pen –
The swill and sweep of Dorset landscape lush
With undulating ribs of green,
The bones your feet trod over beneath fence and trough
When health permitted your energy enough
To walk from Chydyok
The few hundred yards to see the sea knock
And catch the wind from off the bluff
Chalk cliffs at White Nose, Swyre and Bat's Head?

How is it I am found
This summer's day, seventy years on,
Drinking wine with one who knows you well
Though you never met, our feet on the ground
(Flag-stoned) your boots stumbled over – set upon
Rediscovering greater grandeur than this cottage held,
Your now dark eyes showing the sting
The pain a solitary path can bring,
Determined to feast on the natural wild life
Of which the Dorset hills can boast – rife
With canopies of flowers, and echoes of birds' wing,
Living in a manner you knew few humans tried –
Just being, without affectation or side?

How is it I can share this grace bestowed on you?
Share, if just for one day what once you knew
For all time, still unchanged, seen by only a few –
That life at Chydyok was all a man might need
Unless he be a fool and fall for the common greed
Of modern day distractions – those that cut and cause to bleed.

Chesil Beach to New Forest

Lucy Nankivell

I was born by the sea in winter.
White water crashed through my dreams.
Stumbled through childhood, sucking on salty stones.
First silent wish: to be a seagull
and have a voice that cried and cried
the desolation without words.
There were bright days
sun turning pebbles to onyx, jet and silver,
waves playing like blue dolphins.
But I remember grey, and the roar of the stones
and the sea's hungry churning.

I live in a garden edged by forest
trees, gentle tall guardians
catch and play with the tamed wind.
Soft grass, quilted leaves underfoot,
sweet apples above. Yet the roar
is still there, and the hunger
and the gull's cry.

February dawn – Merete Bates

Swannery
Geraldine Farrow

Unnatural on land sitting
on a pile of reeds snarling,

wings splayed huge as a sail
blown fast across the sea,

she hisses threats from her orange bill.
Guiding my child we give her space;

later the same bill turns gently
pale blue eggs beneath her warm belly.

Six grey smudges on top of a nest,
their tall white mother squeaks beneath.

One brave smudge wobbles slowly down,
the others roll, fall to land below.

With unstable legs they cluster,
she walks towards water,

slowly she slips in, the grey huddle watch,
first one, then six, glide on water.

The shore line is swan white, bills bite
others' necks for the best spot.

With a guiding hand my child
flings grain on expectant bills.

A clattering of wings on water
webbed feet paddling a runway,

ungainly lift off for perfect flight.
Hand in hand for the moment,

we watch the swan become
a question mark in the sky.

Portland Bill – Laura Edwards

A Portland life

Jennifer Stewkesbury

The most vivid pictures of the Second World War in my mind are of the bombing raids. Being a naval port and having oil tanks on Portland, we were bound to be bombed. In spite of the blackout, the line of surf along Chesil Beach guided the Germans to their targets. My father having fought in the First World War was too old to be on active service so he joined the Coastguards.

He used to work shifts at the little hut at the top of Church Ope. The beach there was mined and swathes of barbed wire stretched right across from side to side. Later Dad was put on duty at the dockyard and I could sense my mother's anxiety when the siren went. Because Stonycroft was on three floors and that meant a long way up to bed, Dad cut a shelf out of a cupboard in our living room to make space for a bed for me. A bed was brought down for my mother as the room was big enough for that. This living room, called 'the kitchen' from the old days, was the hub of our lives.

Throughout the war we had servicemen or women billeted on us, six at a time. They slept dormitory fashion in one of the big bedrooms on the top floor. They did shift work at the various military establishments on the island. Beds and linen were provided and my mother and grandmother sent the bedclothes to the laundry under the hill. My brother, now nineteen/twenty, left the Admiralty at Bath and joined the army. When he came home on leave he would bring a couple of friends each time. They were all lieutenants and looked very smart in their uniforms and Sam Brownes. We, as a family, all played the piano, my mother being the one who played for the men to sing. One young man called Tubby had a very fine bass voice and to this day I can remember him singing 'Asleep in the Deep' – deep being the significant word. There were also card playing sessions at the big square table in the kitchen. In my hollowed out cupboard space I dozed to the sound of much laughter and the clink of coins. Some beer was drunk but there was never any drunkenness. Granny and Grampy and Uncle Jack did not join in the card games. They all three went to bed after the ten o'clock news. They were always up early, Granny and Grampy to work in the garden and Uncle Jack to work in the dockyard.

The garden was very important to all of us especially during the rationing period. It provided every kind of vegetable and many fruits. There was a large greenhouse on the lower side of the house. It housed ten grapevines which Granny looked after and were heavy croppers of large black grapes. Granny used to paint the vines in early spring with an evil smelling liquid called Gizzard's Compound. This was to keep the dreaded mealy-bug away. As well as the vines, tomatoes were grown and some beautiful flowers – Schizanthus and Cineraria as well as Arum lilies. In the open there were several gardens separated by walls. In one garden were the fruit trees – apple (three kinds), Victoria plum, greengage, golden gage and pear. Rhubarb was grown under tall terracotta towers. Cages protected raspberry canes and strawberry plants. Blackcurrant and gooseberry bushes provided the fruit for a good old Portland favourite, a 'stir-in' – suet pastry crammed with fruit and boiled in a cloth. It was served with sugar and cream. Hugely fattening, but in the rationing very welcome.

In spite of the war, special occasions were celebrated and thoroughly enjoyed. Christmas was notable for the family feasts, achieved by careful housekeeping and good gardening. Another garden which gently sloped towards the railway embankment was planted with vegetables, mostly Portland potatoes which had a flavour never found off the island. Beetroot and onions were always available and in season peas and runner beans. There was a cucumber frame and marrows were grown in there too. Everyone helped in the garden even if it was just to cut some cabbage for friends and relatives. I hated the cabbage patch – caterpillars are not my favourites! Parallel to the vegetable garden was the tennis court and at the bottom of that an enclosed section for chickens. I used to help Granny feed the chickens and was allowed to collect eggs. I didn't much like the cockerel which seemed almost as big as me. Between the fruit garden and the outhouses stood the billiard room.

Being well supplied with fruit, vegetables and eggs it seemed sensible to supplement the meagre meat ration and so we had some bunnies, not as pets but as meat for the table. Over time, chickens were also on the menu and it must have helped in feeding those extra mouths when we were housing the service men and women. At this time, although only six or seven, I gave up taking sugar in tea and have never taken it since. Perversely, with all the fresh food available, I only liked two things, potatoes and cheese! Potatoes were no problem, lots from the garden, but cheese was rationed and I think my parents went short so that I could have more than my share. I was into my teens before I began to eat vegetables. As well as not liking fruit and veg I would not eat fish or meat, and eggs made me sick. Likewise milk. From infancy I had needed half-cream milk, specially ordered from the chemist.

Three incidents during the war years stand out: the first was a particularly sustained bombing raid one night, bad enough for us to leave the house and make our way to the Morrison shelter adjacent to the billiard room. It must have been quite early in the war because I can remember my father carrying me, his feet crunching on the glass that had been blown out of the veranda at the back of the house. The shelter was cold and smelled earthy. Granny, Grampy and Uncle Jack stayed in their beds, very sensible! In daylight we saw that not only had the veranda glass been smashed but most of the greenhouse glass too. The lawn at the back of the house had a liberal sprinkling of shrapnel.

The second incident was quite dramatic. A bomb fell through the roof of a house immediately opposite but did not explode. Some soldiers came to defuse it and found that it had landed on the bed in the front bedroom and the bed clothes had folded around it. Half of Wakeham had to be evacuated. Mum, Dad and I went through the blackout to my Auntie Elsie's (Dad's sister) in Reforne. Granny, Grampy and Uncle Jack refused to budge. I learned later that they had been persuaded to go into the billiard room and get under the table. I wish I had seen that! Those very special soldiers defused the bomb and we were allowed home after lunch the next day.

The third incident was possibly the most serious for me, and the closest I came to a premature death. It must have been in 1941/42, I was five or six. It was afternoon and I was playing with a friend who lived opposite. We had our dollies' prams out. Suddenly the sound of an aeroplane was heard coming from the direction of Pennsylvania Castle. As the sound got louder I was snatched from the pavement by large hands and practically thrown into a narrow passageway between two houses. A black shape hunched over me while in the street could be heard the sound of gunfire. It was over very quickly and the plane flew away northwards. My rescuer returned me to the pavement where I saw my pram in shreds. It did not seem to bother me very much because I was busy telling anyone who would listen that 'I had had an air raid under Mr Stone'. I know that my parents both thanked him for his quick action, and when older and understanding more, I thanked him too; he saved my life. As a post-script it should be added that for my next birthday I received a beautiful doll's pram, fully sprung and in green and cream. I was doubly lucky.

Towards the end of the war Portland saw the arrival of American troops. At first it was all white men and they were friendly to locals, especially children. There were parties for youngsters where unrationed food and sweets were generously distributed. Later black soldiers arrived, and after that there were incidents among the soldiers (generally about local girls), and the atmosphere was not so relaxed. When the troops left the island they left behind dumps of unwanted equipment. There were a lot of lifesavers – an inflatable tyre with a loop to go round the neck and a tape at each end to tie round the waist. Someone got me one of these and as soon as Church Ope Cove opened up I lost no time in getting into the sea with my tyre and I soon learned to swim.

Of course Weymouth and Portland featured importantly in the D-Day offensive. I cannot honestly say that I remember seeing men and ships in large numbers, mainly because I have subsequently seen many images on paper and on screen. I do, however, recall seeing the British and German planes fighting overhead one hot summer. The sky was covered in vapour trails and I can only marvel that not more of them came crashing down nearby. There were one or two, and no one walked away from the aircraft.

St Andrew's graveyard and Rufus Castle, Portland – Scott Irvine

The world has changed; so must Dorset

Benjamin Blech

My essay is a reflection on Dorset's uncertain future in light of growing energy concerns. In November 2010, the International Energy Agency confirmed that production of conventional oil is in decline. Soon afterwards I was home in Lyme Regis, wondering how Dorset would look different if it failed to adapt to a post-oil world. After months of research, this is what I found.

I have always thought Lyme Regis offers everything that's great about Britain; the freedom to roam, stunning views and a culture of long rambling walks only Dorset can provide. It's easy to get lost in the town's laid-back rhythm. That's why anyone who visits always comes back – many stay for good. Having spent much of my life travelling the world, I can still say there's nowhere quite like Lyme Regis.

Despite its unique character and beauty, Dorset is changing fast. Resisting commercialisation was easier in a world where the majority of holiday-makers jetted off to Europe to enjoy the plentiful sunshine, warm waters and cheap wine. That world has changed. This essay outlines why Dorset must now change with it, the problems it faces and what could be done to solve them.

In November 2010, the International Energy Agency (IEA) ended years of speculation by finally admitting that global production of conventional crude oil is in decline. In no uncertain terms it was revealed that, unless governments and individuals do more to curb global oil consumption, by 2035, humans will be using a staggering 99 million barrels a day. With production currently falling at 4% a year and demand still growing steadily, by 2035 the world will only be producing 17 million barrels a day (less than 20% of global demand). With this figure now official, it is no longer inconceivable that oil will soon cost $200 a barrel – ending affordable air travel for the majority. The Channel Tunnel and ferry services would also come at a premium. Add an enormous increase in food prices and holidays abroad are put even further out of reach. One thing is certain; most of us will be spending our holidays closer to home next decade.

Humans are still a long way off implementing a realistic solution to the decline of oil. Finding more oil seems unlikely, with most exploratory drilling around the world resulting in a lot of mud and, relative to global demand, a miniscule amount of oil. If there is oil under Antarctica, it won't be on sale this century. To give an idea of what production would cost, the Deepwater Horizon oil rig, which caught fire in the Gulf of Mexico last year, required about $1 million a day to operate. To replace it will cost $700 million. That's in well-charted, warm seas, a short helicopter flight away from the United States and Mexico. The edge of Antarctica is more than 600 miles from mainland Chile, cut off by freezing, stormy seas and constantly shifting ice. Temperatures in central areas reach −60°C, and 99% of the land is covered in a moving ice sheet, which, on average, is two and a half kilometres thick. There is presently no practical method for drilling through moving ice. Underwater oil terminals would be disrupted by icebergs, some of which are a hundred kilometres wide. With sea levels already rising sharply as the ice melts, turning Antarctica into the world's largest oil field would in any case be a profoundly bad idea.

Reserves of unconventional oil, like oil shale and sands, are plentiful but vastly expensive. They have to be extracted from the ground, transported using some of the largest vehicles on earth, heated with enormous quantities of water, then transported again – all of which requires affordable oil, not to mention 15% higher carbon emissions. Fortunately, mass production remains inconceivable. Why would major oil giants invest trillions installing expensive technologies, paying off massive environmental opposition, all to produce a relatively small quantity of oil for equally small profits?

As for natural gas, the many environmental horror stories show that its risks far outweigh its energy benefits. In any event, without a technological revolution that allows it to be used as a transport fuel, airlines and everyone else will still be dependent on oil at a premium. For a second time, oil will change the face of our existence. The question is, what will this mean for Dorset?

In the next 10 years, as the cost of holidays abroad continues to rise, millions more holidaymakers will arrive in Dorset, as part of an unprecedented boom in domestic tourism. According to the Office for National Statistics (ONS), the number of UK residents taking holidays abroad has been in steady decline since 2009. In 2010, there were nearly 15 million fewer visits abroad by UK residents than in 2006. As global oil production falls and demand continues to grow, this figure is certain to increase dramatically. Consequently, Dorset must adapt to avoid putting unsustainable pressure on local services, communities and the environment.

The impact of a boom in domestic tourism will be particularly significant in Dorset. The area is a safe bet for those with money to invest, with a well-established tourist market that is still the biggest player in the South West, which currently accounts for 20% of all revenue generated by tourism. It has many distinctive locations, giving it limitless potential for marketing and branding. At a time when Britain is heavily in debt, three million people are unemployed, and many capital investors are being drawn to growing Asian markets, rightly or wrongly, the government is coming under increasing pressure to put global economics above conflicting local interests. Dorset is also stunningly beautiful and relatively unspoiled, making it one of Britain's most loved tourist destinations.

Early signs of what is to come are already showing in Lyme Regis, with record numbers of visitors last year and a further rise expected this summer. In 2008, despite mixed feelings among local people, the gap left by the demise of Woolworths was filled with a Tesco, largely aimed at offering more choice to increasing numbers of holidaymakers. Sea defences have been installed at a cost of £21 million, which certainly indicates considerable faith in the market. Change is upon us in Dorset – and here's the good news.

Despite the economic downturn, British tourism is now worth a whopping £115 billion to the national economy, almost 80% of which already comes from the domestic market. A tourism boom will bring millions of pounds to struggling local businesses. As global transportation costs skyrocket, rising food prices will be good news for farmers, as foreign imports no longer act as a cheap alternative to local produce. In no uncertain terms, the housing market will explode upwards, bringing relief to many Dorset residents and ending second homes for all but the super-rich. For Dorset's local economy, the end of the oil era will be very good news indeed.

Despite the economic benefits of the boom, Dorset is ill equipped to accommodate millions more visitors each year. To protect what visitors come to enjoy, action must be taken to minimise the impact on Dorset's environment and communities. With the decline of conventional oil now official, it seems unlikely that many visitors will be driving to Dorset in 2035. Gas, electric and solar powered cars will not be affordable to the majority for at least twenty years. Emission-free biofuels may soon be available but will be needed to power agricultural machinery, essential to feeding a rapidly growing population. There simply isn't the space to grow the cleaner equivalent of 99 million barrels of oil a day. Massive investment in public transport is therefore needed. In some cases, this will mean wider roads in order to avoid the chaos and pollution caused by coaches trundling down roads built for horse and cart. An environmentally sound, high-speed railway network which serves all major tourist destinations must be reinstated. By relaying new track along routes that have already been cut (the tracks were torn up under Margaret Thatcher), road modifications can be kept to a minimum, preserving Dorset's environment and rural character.

To minimise the impact visitors have after they arrive, local government must make eco-tourism a priority, working towards 100% eco-friendly output by 2035. This will be expensive by almost any standards, but considering visitor numbers will at least triple, it is still affordable. To meet the cost, higher taxation, alongside a more moral foundation to our capitalist economy, must play a part in Dorset's future. From now on, anyone wanting to open for business in a premium area like Dorset should contribute to eco-tourism, in proportion to the size of their business and capital. It is simply not right that the taxpayer should meet the brunt of a higher tax bill, while billion-pound corporations enjoy the benefits of a premium area without making large contributions to its well-being.

The development of greener tourism is already close at hand in Dorset, with the construction of many eco-homes which, with larger government subsidies and advances in technology, could lead to new eco-hotels and restaurants. There is also great potential for new outdoor activity centres, with a variety of gradients for cycling tours, hard-rock cliffs for climbing and abseiling, stunning walking trails, beautiful coastline and, relative to much of the country, plenty of sunshine. In fact, in terms of its potential for eco-tourism, Dorset is simply unbeatable.

There are also a number of social issues that will come with a domestic tourism boom. At least 50% of the workforce must be sourced from the local area to ensure local people benefit from the unprecedented prosperity. In order to prevent the development of hotspots of violence and antisocial behaviour, existing alcohol licensing laws must be rethought, to avoid high concentrations of pubs opening in the same area[1]. An equal spread of upmarket resorts, cheaper hotels and a wide range of shops and restaurants will also ensure Dorset remains on the map as a county that can offer something for everyone. Lastly, while we should not discourage much-needed investment, local people's interests must be given precedence over the aspirations of business. They should therefore be given greater say in the kind of businesses that will benefit their community, putting David Cameron's doubtful 'Big Society' to the ultimate test.

To conclude, many challenges lie ahead for Dorset, but with careful planning the future is bright. Before local interests can be protected, we must accept the decline of oil as a global event, soon to change our lives in ways difficult to imagine. Now is the time to be informed on the facts and bring the transition away from oil, into our everyday lives. Only by doing so will Dorset and the world have a sustainable future.

---

1. The 2003 Licensing Act removed the long-standing requirement for new alcohol licence holders to prove the need for an additional licensed premise. In the absence of a valid objection, which, by way of wealth and connections, rarely reaches a courtroom, all applicants are automatically granted a licence. Many researchers have found that this has led to centres of excessive drinking, violence and antisocial behaviour.

Walking the dogs in Bournemouth – Maria Konstanse Bruun

Wedding dress

Claire Wyburn

Casey crouched inside the hedge. The air was still, the leaves were still. So still, she wondered if they were plastic. Nothing about today felt real. She touched one of the leaves, held it tight between her finger and thumb, until she could feel it breathe.

'Talk to me,' she whispered. 'Show me where Sean is.'

The leaf said nothing.

Beyond the hedge, the wedding guests chatted. Snippets of polite conversation crawled into her ears; she pressed her hands against them. She didn't want to hear any of it. This wasn't the wedding they had planned, her and Sean. They'd wanted to get hitched at The Burning Man Festival in Arizona, high on acid and house music. Sean had always paid far too much attention to what his mum wanted. Bloody Brenda.

Casey swigged from the bottle of sherry beside her feet, taking care not to rustle the leaves. She couldn't afford to be caught in here, inside the dog's bolt-hole. She had to pick her moment. She needed to wait for Sean. Through the leaves, she watched guests she didn't recognise picking at nibbles from the long feast table under the giant oak. She scanned strangers mingling on the lawn, squinting at each other underneath a violent sun. Still no Sean.

It was hot, even for July. Casey's feet were sweating inside her strappy sandals. Soil stuck to her toe nails. She hadn't varnished them, not that Sean would notice. He wasn't superficial like that. Brenda would, though. Casey's legs ached, but she couldn't sit down. She didn't want to ruin Sean's special dress. Oh where was he? Casey scanned the crowd again. Brenda swished out of the patio doors in a flowing yellow dress, bright as the sun. She was carrying a four-tier wedding cake with the usual plastic couple on top – bride in white gown, groom in black top and tails.

Well, Casey was wearing purple, not white!

Brenda walked down the garden with the cake. Casey willed her to trip and fall, cake first, with her smug face slap on top of it. But Brenda reached the table safely. She put the cake down and spoke to the vicar, now standing beside her. He had his fingers stuffed into his collar, as if it was choking him. Or maybe he was about to pull out a cross so he could exorcise Brenda, the demanding mother-in-law from hell. Casey sniggered. She took another swig of sherry, then turned her attention back to the garden.

Casey spotted him straight away. Her Sean. He stood head-and-shoulders above the crowd, so tall he seemed to melt into the sky. He was wearing a bright blue shirt speckled with tiny white flowers. Casey knew he wouldn't be wearing black. She felt a rush of love run through her.

'It's time,' the leaves said, 'go to him.'

Casey pushed forward. A branch scraped her cheek. She winced. It wasn't as easy to get out of the hole as it was to get in. Through the leaves, Sean was laughing. He was laughing with a chubby man in a black trilby. Eddie. His best mate. His best man.

'Go,' the leaves insisted.

The leaves and Sean and Eddie swarmed in and out of Casey's vision. She hitched her dress up past her knees and crawled out of the hedge.

'Sean,' Casey cried, still on her hands and knees. 'I'm here.'

The garden fell silent. Everyone turned round. A drop of blood fell from Casey's cheek onto the sleeve of her dress. She sat back on her heels. She wiped her cheek with her hand. She focused on Sean. Her fiancé, her lover. He was walking towards her, his long, long legs getting closer.

Casey put her arms up; longing tugged on her belly. She waited for his touch.

But Sean did not touch her. He stopped a few feet short of her.

'See!' Casey smoothed her dress down over her knees again. 'I'm wearing the dress you bought me the day you proposed, remember? You said it was lovely.' Casey looked up at Sean, shielding her face from the sun with her hands. 'You said it was precious, like me.'

Sean's eyes travelled down the dress, slowly. He did not meet her gaze.

'I miss those holidays in Thailand, don't you?' Casey wanted to hug him, to kiss him. But she couldn't stand up right now. She was too giddy with love.

'What are you doing here, Casey?' Sean kept his eyes on the grass.

'I've come to take you away, to Arizona.'

'What?' Sean's eyes darted up to her face.

Casey met his gaze, at last. It was like diving into a mountain pool, gazing into Sean's eyes. They were dark, deep, invigorating. 'That was the wedding we planned,' she smiled.

Sean didn't smile back. 'You're still drunk.'

'A little,' Casey giggled. 'I'm still your child of the forest, though. Let's go back to the old days. We could live in our tent again, out in the New Forest.'

Sean moved a few steps closer. He crouched down beside her, one knee on the grass. Casey wondered if he was going to propose to her all over again.

'Have you lost the plot?' Sean said the words so quietly, Casey could barely hear them. 'You disappeared three years ago. I spent ages thinking you were dead. I ...' he put his head in his hands and sighed, 'I've moved on.' He dropped his hands away from his face and met her eyes again.

'I love you.' Casey pulled a twig out of her hair. 'I can't let you go through with this.'

'If you love me, then you won't ruin my wedding day. You'll leave before Joanne gets here.'

'She's just the rebound.'

'Maybe, at first. But not now.'

Casey held his gaze. She could feel it, the tenderness rising up from the depths of those rock pools of his. 'I see love in your eyes.'

Sean shook his head, slowly. 'No, you see pity. It hurts me to see you like this.'

Panic churned Casey's belly. She couldn't think straight. 'No,' she insisted. 'You love me. Look! I'm still wearing your ring.' She held her left hand up. There was a white band of skin on her engagement finger – but no ring. Casey stared at her hand. Where had the ring gone? She'd put it on this morning. She was sure of it. She checked her other hand. There was no ring. But her finger nails were ragged and caked in dirt. The skin on her fingers was flaking. There were scabs on her knuckles. She blinked. This wasn't how she'd looked this morning, was it?

Suddenly, Casey became aware of the burning sun, of the guests staring at her, of Brenda's voice shouting, over and over – I've called the police, I've called the police. And Eddie too, he was at her back, trying to lift her up. She couldn't hear what he was saying. She felt sick. She was thirsty. 'I'm wearing your special dress. Remember the day we bought it, the day you proposed to me?'

'Yes,' Sean sighed.

Eddie hauled her up. He kept one arm behind her back. 'C'mon, Casey, it's time to go.'

Casey tried to wriggle free from Eddie, but he was too strong. 'Touch me, please,' she said to Sean. She put her free hand out. 'Touch me one last time.'

Sean touched her hand. Casey closed her eyes. She held his hand tight, until she could feel the blood pumping inside him. Sean pulled his hand away. Casey opened her eyes. Sean's mountain pools were cold. He turned away and walked towards the house.

Eddie dragged her, backwards, to the bottom of the garden. 'Your personal escort's here, Casey.' He pushed her into the backseat of the police car and slammed the door. The locks went. Shock shook Casey. Her body sobered up. She longed for more sherry. Only she wasn't going to get it in here, inside a police car.

'You been making a nuisance of yourself again, eh?'

Casey met the driver's gaze in the rear-view mirror. The way he was looking at her, it reminded her of Sean. Back there, in the garden. No, it couldn't be true. She shook her head and squeezed her eyes shut. Sean loved her.

'Carry on like this and you'll end up in jail, or dead. We can put you in touch with Bournemouth's Drug and Alcohol Team. Get you into a treatment centre.'

Casey screwed her nose up at the driver's reflection. She'd already tried rehab. Sean had put her on the train from London to Bournemouth. He held her hand so tight she thought he'd never let her go. He promised they'd get married as soon as she was better. But she got kicked out after a week. She called Sean to say she was coming home, then went to the pub. She never got on the train.

The driver turned his attention back to the road, leaving Casey with her reflection. Her eyes were bloodshot. Dirt streaked her face. Thread veins scoured her cheeks. Deep scratches penetrated her lips, like rivers of blood. Disgust shrivelled her belly. Her fingers quivered, her legs jumped. 'Are you going to let me out in Boscombe?'

The driver met her eyes again. 'Sorry, love. You're in no fit state to walk the streets. You're in a cell for the night. It's for your own safety.'

This time, Casey confronted the pity in his eyes. The same pity she'd seen in Sean. She knew that now. She wanted to tell the driver how she used to be a fashion writer. That she'd interviewed the likes of Ralph Lauren and Stella McCartney. But her throat burned. She clasped her hands together and put her head down. She tried to retreat to Thailand, back to the day Sean proposed. She needed to feel his love inside her heart forever. But her head was a mess and her heart was cold. The memories of a thousand nights of sleeping rough underneath the subway by Asda jumbled through her mind. She didn't want to think about the ugly faces of tramps she'd slept with inside scummy sleeping bags, or the sexual assaults in squats off Christchurch Road.

She found herself staring, really staring, at the dress Sean had given her to wear on their wedding day. The material was filthy and threadbare. It looked like ashes, sewn together. As if she was wrapped up in a cremation. Casey shuddered. She remembered now, what had happened to the ring. She'd pawned it for drugs. She couldn't remember which shop it was in. Anyway, Sean was right. That was a long time ago, so long, it would be long gone. Loneliness pinched Casey's heart.

She watched her tears fall onto the dress. She was so thin, she could see her ribs and nipples poking through it. She realised she wasn't crying for Sean anymore. She was crying for herself. She didn't want to put herself through another night on the streets. She wanted her body and her mind back. She lifted her head up and gently touched the driver's shoulder. 'Can you really help me?'

'Yes,' he said. 'Everything will be alright, you'll see.'

St George's Church, Portland – Scott Irvine

High Dorset

Paddy Hughes

Summer snaffles a chunk of Dorset's autumn.
The Downs still field a dawn of sun-scuffed dust,
their mounds and hollows heaving sensuously
to the lovings of the coast and laughing
into folds of distant vapour.

On top of Eggardon exotic kites surf an Iron Age wave
and a Roman highway breathes with ghosts.
Legions of pylons stride the shimmering hills
with shoulder-loads of power and paint fingers
of shadow for cows to cool in.

At Compton Valence centuries of sheep have carved
a corduroy of paths below a thorn-rimmed lip.
The steep amphitheatre traps the eye and plunges
from the gods to a stage anchored by the bulk
of busy blocks of farm.

A whirl of gulls salts the sky
and butterflies sprinkle pepper.

Another stolen day unrolls.

Memory

Janet Hancock

'*This* is the spot,' says Richie. The wind off the sea cuts across his face. Tang of salt and weed fills his nostrils. He burrows into the neck of his coat. The chair wheels squelch to a halt on wet shingle, the back pulling taut as Jan secures the brakes. Nice lad, Jan. He spells it with a 'J' but pronounces it with a 'Y'. 'Yan,' he enunciated, as if teaching a child, the first time he arrived at the nursing home to take Richie out. Ban, can, Dan, Richie thought, and worked through the alphabet. H, k, l, s didn't make words; x and z didn't really count.

Every Wednesday afternoon, Jan comes to his room. Sometimes Jan wheels him to the park or recreation ground. Richie enjoys watching children shrieking and fighting on swings and roundabouts. His kids used to be like that. The only difference is in those days youngsters went on their own. Now, adults – grandparents, most probably – are watching, vigilant. Other times, same as today, Jan drives him in the van, with a ramp at the back for the chair.

'Which is it to be, Richie?' Jan always asks. Richie likes that, as though he has some control.

'Down to the beach, below the headland,' he told Jan when the lad arrived after lunch.

Jan looked through the window of Richie's room, brow furrowing. 'You'll need your hat and coat on.'

Richie helped Jan as much as arthritic arms and wrists would let him. They got the sleeves in place, and Jan pulled up the zip, settled the coat down Richie's back and sides.

'Chilly wind,' Jan told him. 'Still only April.' He reached for Richie's cap on the back of the door and set it gently on his head as if testing the fit. Richie liked that. Jan didn't ram it on, another job done, let's be off and get it over with. Jan pushed green knitted mittens over the gnarls, bumps and talons that insisted they were Richie's hands.

Jan comes from Poland, wants to work in information technology, I.T. – 'computers, Richie,' he explained during their first afternoon outing – but for the moment toils in the kitchen of a restaurant in town – 'vegetables, Richie, peeling, scraping, chopping: when chef shouts, they have to be ready' – sending money to his widowed mother in Cracow. Jan always smells of garlic. Richie knows about garlic.

'We had a lot of Polish airmen on our squadron in the war,' he told Jan. Richie lifted his head as far as his neck would allow, found Jan's smiling brown eyes, wondered if Jan believed him, that he used to fly Spitfires, one of the Brylcreem Boys.

But Jan said, 'My grandfather could have been one of them.'

There are steps from the headland down to the beach, and a zig-zag path the length of the biscuit-coloured cliff-face. Richie had the urge to say, 'Let go of the chair, then I can free wheel. It's the nearest I'll ever get to flying.' Instead, he asked Jan, 'Do you think there are any fossils?'

'We'll come in the summer and dig around, shall we?' Jan suggested. 'See what we can find.'

At the foot of the cliff is a hollow, a bower in the sand for two people. Every year he and Maya used to come here, a couple of miles from their bungalow, on the anniversary of when they met. He'd gone to France with some friends a few years after the war, when the cemeteries were first established. They stayed in a village boarding house; Maya was working in her parents' bakery. For months after his return, they wrote to each other and Richie joined an evening class to improve his French. Twice he went back to France, and the wedding was arranged.

When they used to come here on their anniversary, sometimes it was windy like today, other times warm sunshine, one of those early spring days with much promise. They took a photograph of each other every year, in the hollow, and then he got one of those cameras where you can set it and rush back to be in the picture. He has all the photos, an archive of encroaching grey hair, wrinkled skin hanging more loosely on a creaking frame, enduring love. After the photograph, they would walk hand in hand to the water's edge and wave to the ferry that had just left Weymouth.

'*I wonder by my troth, what thou and I did till we loved*,' Maya used to quote from John Donne in her rich velvety voice; she always had trouble with 'th'. She had read the line somewhere, copied it out in her elegant schoolgirl handwriting, stuck it on the fridge in the kitchen. They didn't come last year or the one before. Maya got that she didn't know him, poor darling, white wispy hair and pink scalp where once there'd been raven curls which took his breath away the first time he walked into that village bakery across the Channel for *pain au chocolat*. Until she died during the winter, he would sit in their bungalow holding hands whose purple veins protruded through skin the texture of tissue paper; hands that used to chide and cherish three children, used to dust, hoover, wash, iron, garden, cook; hands that touched him, knew him, loved him. He managed, with carers: Doreen, Naomi, Pam, brisk young women in navy trousers and uniform tunics, watch face and name badge clipped onto breast pocket. 'And how are we today?' as if Maya and the carer were one.

'You got a girlfriend?' he ventured as Jan wheeled him past the hollow and onto the shingle.

'Nah,' Jan replied, a long sound that wished it were something else. 'Girls only out for themselves,' he added.

The wind is relenting, white horses giving way to lace frills rippling to the chair wheels. He takes several breaths of salt and seaweed air as if he must store some; lifts his head as far as he can. No ferry today.

'Nice bit of sea air,' comments Jan.

The lad must wonder why we've come here, Richie thinks, and he closes his eyes, can smell Maya's perfume, a whiff of orange blossom. '*I wonder by my troth, what thou and I did till we loved,*' he says, hardly giving the words voice, letting white lace caps carry them away.

Jan bends down to him and all Richie can see is a hat knitted like a rainbow. 'What was that, Richie?'

'John Donne.' His eyes are faltering towards sleep but later he'll tell Jan about the poet.

'*I wonder by my troth, what thou and I did till we loved,*' Jan quotes.

Richie's eyes blink open. He raises his head, sees on Jan's face a questioning expression that hopes he's got it right.

Abandoned – Katie Stenhouse

Shepherd's warning
Andy Case

I saw the old man on the hill,
A silhouette,
The pale sun behind his head.
He turned to me and pointed there
And I remembered what he said;
'It allus raines tomorrow
When thic zun goes pale to bed,
We'll 'ave to chop they mangels
In barn, in dry, instead'.

September love
Andy Case

When the raine pawrs down
An' I cassunt werk the land
Fer seeds to zow,
An' the puddeled laine
Wi all the raine
A rivulet do flow,
An' the brooding trees
Wi zodden leaves
Bend their backs loike an aarcher's bow,
As lashed wi raine
As if in paine
Their branches sweep so low,
Zo I look at the sky
An' heave a zigh
An' wish this storm would goo,
Fer on a day loike this
It would be bliss
To goo to beed wi you,
Fer I remember
Laarst September
They werds you zaid s' slow
That rainy days
Be loving days
An' evermore be zo.

Odd encounter in Shaftesbury

Timmy Crump

I seldom speak to strangers in the street
but walking through the churchyard into town
(a short-cut, green and peaceful, lined with limes)
saw oldish man, standing patiently
with lead in hand, the other end a dog,
black and looking older than the man.

What intrigued me most was that the dog
was smelling snowdrops (winter on the wane).
I said: 'I thought that snowdrops didn't smell.'

The man replied, quite seriously: 'Well,
The dog's stone deaf you see.' I had to say:
'Of course, that would explain it,' and went my way.

Lone tree – Emma Foot

Susan Henchard, Dorchester Fair, 1886
Pam Kelly

Her eyes downcast, her face
a blush of shame
her loss of pride competing with
the growing fear that this
might be for real,
she stood there in the market-place
amid the sheep and cows
for sale in Casterbridge.
She held her baby tight-clutched
to her breast, so she could feel
some comfort that might guard
against the sights and sounds
from those who stood around
with mocking jeers
and pointing at this wife
her husband wished to sell.
What hell had she unleashed
that life could be this bitter hard
and husbands be so cruel and
unpredictable?

In the priory graveyard
Lesley Burt

Fairground sounds,
the scent of onions,
waft from the quayside;

headstones lean
like watchful mothers
over bones blanketed by turf.

A man in baseball cap
and ear defenders mows graves:
beheads a crop of pushed-up daisies.

Ringstead Beach reflections – Rosy Emberley

Never forget
Frederick Rea Alexander

'Never forget' I heard the boy tell me,
but already I was forgetting what
him and I had shared underneath night's sea,
his eyes now grey and empty of life, but
I still felt that fire within that burned me
When we were once hand grenades and stone hearts,
And we broke each other as we knew we must
For in embrace were we furthest apart.

So 'Never forget' may be too much
For how could I forget the boy who won
What others had tried and failed, as such
Was my heart, my love and my soul undone.

And I knew under stars, with love and lies,
I would never forget his cold grey eyes.

Burnt
Frederick Rea Alexander

I sat and looked out over the charred heathland. Gorse and
sand mingled beneath my hands. Above, an eagle circled
on a wave of heat, spying, waiting.

'Do you think it'll ever be the same?' he asked.

I looked down at my leg.

'Give it time.'

Nautical map

Helen Pizzey

Its details flat and colourless:
dull yellows in waves
and shoals of nameless blues;
tides of pluses and low minuses
to make the non-numeric shiver.

Can this be bone and skin
of earth and oceans meeting,
this lifeless demarcation
of islands, rivers, shore?

And so cold?

I picture the soft contours
of the reed that's bent by sunlight,
a sultriness of skyline,
warm tilt of seabird's wing;

a waterscape that's mine by touch,
each bend and reach a furrow:
merging lines soft-etched and plotted
on live parchment of my bows.

'Where are you to?'

Valerie Bridge

'Where are you to?'
he asked, searching over his shoulder,
the mobile stiff in his leathered palm,
his farming eyes listening,
eyeing the straightness of his electric fence,
adding the cost of the pillar-box red generator
he's just got, to the turnover, the stock, the barley,
the hay he's going to sell early, to that he'll keep
stacked, waiting for the price to rise,
his barn's alive with skylarks larking through
on a wing and a prayer, his fields pricked by rabbit ears,
not so many hares of late, and a still horse on the edge
of the far field outlined by sunset, and the breath streaming
out of his flared baby-soft nostrils, the quiver of his flanks
rising, falling, and he will tell me none of this yet,
waiting, wanting the call to end, needing to get on,
and still he's urgent with his wanting, his breath
escaping his wet lip, and his hard palm
softening on 'Where are you to?'

Bees – Alicia Chambers-Hill

Forgotten uses of furze

Nigel Palfrey

The shadows in my mind grow longer with the passing years, causing many memories to drift beyond recall. Other more recent ones remain less focused as they too glide away on a stream of fading consciousness. One old memory, a constant companion, is no longer sharpened by anticipation for I often visit the dream as an adult that was so cherished when young. I cannot say precisely when it started nor state it is finished and truly a memory, for each time I visit the downlands the dream is revisited. Here I walk the chalk and talk the talk of wild flowers while hearing the wind amongst gold-flowered bushes.

My childhood vision began while visiting relatives living near chalk streams feeding the River Frome. There, obscured by waving weed, silver ghosts swam in crystal clear waters. They were of course Grayling – the 'lady of the waters' – which fought like street fighters when hooked and tasted as a lady should taste. Those visits included walking 'the heights', as the grassed downs were called, and here you filled your lungs with fresh air as you laboured up or came disjointedly down the hillsides while travelling narrow sheep paths. The paths follow the contours assiduously while their ridged edge supplied you with a variety of green-leaved grasses and other plants, whose flower heads made identification easier.

It was here on these hillsides that I first came into contact with furze – a synonym for gorse. The plant is much maligned but holds my admiration for I know now many of its true values, having seen it furnish support for wildlife, people's wages and wood heat for many a fire. My introduction to furze came through Humphrey, often referred to as Hump or 'Old Pearce', for he was indeed ancient to my young eyes. I remember him principally for furze cutting and bundling faggots, but you usually saw him repairing stone-work and hedges or sometimes directing the forming of cob and flint walls. It was he, after we had erected hanging and latching oak gate posts, who said the deliberately charred ends in the ground should last at least 50 years.

Now when I lean on a well hung gate more than half a century later those remembered words ring true. Humphrey was always my idea of the character Gabriel Oak in Thomas Hardy's *Far From the Madding Crowd*. An early recollection of Humphrey was on a sheep path repairing a hedge at the flanks of a steep combe. In his prime a tall thickset man, now slightly stooped with thick grey hair, a florid complexion and grey eyes that observed the smallest detail and looked directly at you. When asked if I had seen a linnet's nest, I stood above the path while gnarled hands held a staff hook and gently bent a furze bush. I then gazed down to a woven grass cup lined with sheep's wool and scarcely visible fine hair. It held four light blue and dark-spotted eggs that I was told were 'more precious than gemstones'. He also informed me that the female was the nest builder, sometimes having three broods often communally; while the quiet twitter with odd pure notes from the male was sometimes sung in chorus. That was really the measure of the man, for his knowledge of goings-on in country life was encyclopaedic and I was eager to learn.

Humphrey taught me the elementary skills in hedge laying and the rudiments of dry-stone walling, for only practice over time will lead to craftsmanship. He instilled in me the ability to stand back and take an objective view of the tasks ahead, for some would not be undertaken for months or years. His philosophy became apparent with remarks such as 'It's all about thinking ahead of you' and, to the work-rate, as 'Best going along quietly'. Another remark was 'Here today and gone tomorrow' when tasks had been accomplished in a slapdash fashion, for this Blandford-bred man believed that properly executed work was synonymous with enduring qualities. Now that I approach his age, I understand more clearly the meaning of showing young people correct procedures and the pleasure he gained when a 'greenhorn' exhibited budding skills. I thought of him after watching a young man correctly re-lay Portland capping stone inside St Paul's Cathedral and then smiled to myself. I more often thought of him when returning wartime airfields to the plough, or forming roadways and new housing estates, for so often we removed or cut furze. Quite often the people employed took an interest in their work; a few like Humphrey had that rarer interest in natural history and awareness of historical surroundings.

Humphrey helped nurture in me a deeper understanding of the countryside he knew; his working life had followed the River Frome upstream from Wareham to beyond Dorchester. I wondered who his relatives were around Tincleton and were any of those 'the Dorsetshires' killed in Korea in the 1950s. If you saw an isolated furze plant in an unexpected place, Humphrey would say the seed had remained dormant in the soil for decades until disturbed. Or remark that a hundred years earlier the vegetation may well have been heath and scrub, especially the 'sideling' ground that horse and oxen could not plough. The seedlings of common furze start as spineless shamrock shapes with few true leaves; they compensate for this by surrounding themselves in a mass of green growth culminating in ridged linear spines of various lengths. Each yellow-tipped spine points at a different angle from a neighbour and later the plant branches out. By that stage sheep and rabbit tend to leave the plant alone due to high concentration of the noxious alkaloid ulexine. The main flowering period is springtime when ant, fly and bumble bee visit the flowers, with early and late nocturnal visits by beetle and moth. If it is warm enough honey bees visit the flowers which smell of coconuts and you observe them retuning to the hive threshold with baskets of orange pollen; such useful early brood food. The plant will grow to ten feet high often in conjunction with other furze species like western furze at Warmwell, which has deeper golden yellow flowers during July to October. Another and not dissimilar species is dwarf furze of Wareham heath, this flowers best between August and September and the honey bee can more easily reach down the shorter throat of the last two species should a 'nectar flow' occur. The resultant honey hints of coconut, reminding me of sitting in the welcome shade of furze on 'the heights' during a summer day where a breeze filters through heat waves and linnet or skylark sing their wistful songs. You can replicate this at other places such as Offa's Dyke at Hergest Ridge, the Forest of Bowland or certain ridgeways in Hampshire; for furze grows in every county in Britain, even in the low lands of Thetford Forest or stony riverside near Warmwell.

Furze wood is surprisingly heavy, for the yellowish close grain creates dense material. The fire wood rapidly splits and shakes when drying yet rarely throws a spark onto my open hearth, while the volatile oils in twigs and foliage ensure it fires quickly when used as kindling. I saw my last true faggot stack of ash and furze wood while driving down the hill into Branscombe, Devon, and knew I was witnessing a disappearing way of life. The bakery would close before the brushwood roof of furze heads and heather was burnt. I stopped on this occasion to observe a furze head burn in a bread oven. The foliage was once part of the roof, but in the country you expect little to be wasted and organic materials have alternate uses – something Humphrey approved of! Once the foliage reduced to fine light grey ash, it was brushed out with another furze twig and replaced with twice-kneaded dough, then allowed to rise while the baker slept before the next bake. When a 'bake was on,' the oven hearth would be fired with bavins (small faggots) that burnt with a steady but intense heat until reduced to a small residue of ash. Other timbers when burnt rarely reach such quick or prolonged temperatures and most reduce, leaving significant tar and ash residue. At home that evening the base of my loaves had a dusting of furze ash; however, this ash is mild to the taste buds, unlike the ash of other woods.

By the close of a working day cutting furze, the loose pile of assorted stems thrown to a 'pike' would have steadily grown. Due to soil type, age of plants and ease of access, it will at best produce 24 large faggots and 12 'bavins' (short lengths) from an area 22 paces by 6 paces (one chain × one rod). This old-fashioned measurement is a surprisingly accurate method to pace out on site and reflects the results from the average day's labour on the average site. Humphrey understood such mundane things and they were implicit in his teachings. Obviously furze grown in infertile soil or under ten years of age will at best produce short faggots, each stem up to 9 barley corns thick (3 inches or 75 mm). Large faggot stems measure to 3 ft long (1 metre) and up to 12 inches (15–30 cm) in circumference. After a day's labour, Humphrey often slung a 'bavin' over his shoulder for his winter fire and walked off 'the heights' as though out for a daily stroll. After curing outdoors in summer, a large faggot loses a quarter of its weight due to water loss and is then sawn for sticks or logs, kept dry and used at the onset of autumn. I burn one large faggot on the evening hearth and when heat saturates the room with a whiff of wood-smoke, it causes a hand to feel the dogs beside your chair, making the previous hard work worthwhile.

During a summer day clearing scrub in the 1980s, I sat in shade cast by birch saplings while an erstwhile friend spoke of a Norfolk boyhood at Bungay. He recalled making fishing line from the 'bast' (inner bark) of furze and then proceeded to make fibrous line from freshly cut furze. I surprised a water bailiff recently with the strength of a thin tapering fishing line some 12 inches long, thinner than but as strong as honeysuckle twine! I remember sowing furze seed by hand and racking in small brown kidney shapes to germinate and add greenery in a landscape of rock scree. The same process happened in sections of embankments on the M3/27 motorway and A31 road. It's an ancient method – some for the wind, some for the crow, some to wither and some to grow. There are small beetles that rely on furze as their food plant and caterpillars of moths called the Lead Belle and July Belle. Adult moths can be disturbed while walking in furze between May to August and then you observe these nondescript moths from afar but wonder at their beautiful spots, lines and grey-brown shades when closely observed. The Green Hairstreak butterfly lays its eggs on furze. The creature's upper brown wings remind me of Humphrey for he always wore brown corduroy trousers and brown jackets. When settled on green furze foliage the butterfly closes its wings and vanishes like Humphrey did when working in the furze; for the butterfly has green undersides and it too becomes a memory.

Sometimes, while sitting beside furze, I recite John Keats' poem, 'Old Meg she was a Gipsy and liv'd upon the Moors/ Her bed it was the brown heath turf,/ And her house was out of doors./ Her apples were swart blackberries,/ Her currants pods o' broom;/ Her wine was dew of the wild white rose,/ Her book a churchyard tomb.' I rarely remember the remaining words but my dogs never worry when I stop talking aloud!

The bridge

Judy Bannon

The village square is quiet. I side-step a couple in matching cagoules as they mooch along the narrow pavement and stride towards the stark ruins of the castle. Pewter clouds hang heavy above the bridge across the dry moat. I grip the wooden barrier as I stare down into the ditch, the weathered-grain of oak forms rough ridges under my fingers. This is the place where we had our first kiss, one year ago today; then I could hear the sound of banqueting in the great hall and the laughter of lovers dancing, today I hear the howling of the wind.

He had driven his moss-coloured MG along the narrow road at the base of the steep chalk mound, accelerating out of each bend with childish delight. As we approached the centre of the village the warm wind played with the lavender and lilies in the cottage gardens, brushing them against each other in brief caresses, releasing their musky scent. Mark had described Corfe to me in great detail; the soft grey of the stone cottages, the church dedicated to the murdered King Edward on the edge of the village square and the imposing castle ruins.

Self-consciously we linked hands and strolled past the knee-high ledges of the oily-glazed windows. I ducked down, giggling, to peek into the private interiors; tiny rooms filled with antique furniture and family photographs.

We reached a gift shop and Mark tugged me inside, picking out a key-ring tagged with a carved wooden 'K'.

'Come on, Kathryn, let me buy it for you; the dark wood is the colour of your eyes and it's smooth and curvy just like you.'

Shouts and laughter focus my eyes back into the dusty moat and I look up from the ditch to see a teenage boy and girl racing down the hill towards me; as they rush by I feel invisible. My stomach aches for the sweetness of that kiss, the intensity in his sapphire eyes and the warmth of his arms around me. With a concerted effort I pull my dull legs slowly towards the fractured archway of the gatehouse. The wind picks up, swirling through the fallen stones, as the air freshens before rain and I can almost hear the shouts of soldiers and the clatter of hooves over the worn cobbles. The clouds lose their battle to hold moisture and I take shelter in an old doorway, reaching into a crevice to steady myself.

'Let me hold you.' Mark's words are snatched away by the wind.

It is two months and eleven days since I have seen him and I spent yesterday in bed feeling too depressed to leave my flat. But this morning I gave myself one of those 'pull yourself together' chats and made the decision to come back here in an attempt to exorcise the ghosts.

There is a break in the rain. I wander up to the old Keep and the familiar view of Poole harbour spreading out its craggy fingers into the surrounding heathland. Shafts of sunlight pierce the clouds, linking the sky to the earth, ephemeral spokes of shining clarity against the grey. The sound of thunder echoes like the distant sound of fighting that destroyed these castle walls centuries ago.

Our arguments seem so stupid, full of the usual carelessly thrown comments and hurtful smart remarks.

'I thought we were trying to save!'

'Don't tell me how to spend my money; you know how important my car is to me.'

His car had broken down on the way to visit his sister in Dorchester and the subsequent repairs ate up a large part of our savings. The niggling had gradually mounted over the next few days.

'We were supposed to be looking at houses this weekend.'

'Yes, but we can't afford it.'

'It wasn't me who spent so much of the money for our house on a broken-down old car.'

That was it, he slammed the phone down and I haven't heard from him since. My stupid pride won't let me contact him. We had promised each other that we would be living in our new house before Christmas. Now I'm dreading Christmas.

A raven squawks as it leaves its perch in one of the arrow slits and, as I look up, my mobile vibrates in my pocket. I press the button while my eyes follow the raven to its new position on the ragged edge of the Keep wall.

'I'm sorry, M.'

I swallow hard.

'Where R U?' I text back.

Then it rings. 'Hi ... Sorry ... I've been really selfish.'

Before I can reply, 'I'll be with you in five minutes.'

'But, how do you know where I am?'

'I can hear the ravens and the wind ... and besides, where else would you be today?'

My legs are light as I race down the hill and I smile as I pass a couple in matching blue cagoules. These proud stones hold powerful memories and the promise of continuity well into the future. The gatehouse frames the bridge as it had once framed the lowered drawbridge and I feel like Lady Mary Bankes welcoming home her lover as I see Mark leaning against the wooden railings.

Hello, pretty damsel, can I cadge a lift?'

'Where's your car?'

'That old thing, I've sold it.'

'I suppose I can't refuse a knight in distress, but only after you've bought me lunch in the pub.'

Moses saving the Israelites, St Basil's Church, Toller Fratrum – Bronwen Coe

Fitz's story

Megan Cannon

Since his mother had abandoned him at the age of eight, Fitz had been housed, fostered and provided for by the local authority, but at the age of sixteen he had been abandoned again to fend for himself. He had managed quite well, surviving on benefits, begging, petty shoplifting and opportunistic thieving. He believed that during his dealings with police, magistrates and probation officers, his manner and appearance created the impression that he was a cut above the rest, so saving him from prison; he had always managed to talk his way out of other situations. Fitz himself despised the rest of the jobless and aimless guys who circled in and around Dorchester, who disappeared from time to time then reappeared, often with unmistakable prison pallor showing whence they had returned. Fitz never joined them when they decamped to Weymouth in the summer. He knew that there was no gain to be had there, only harassment from the locals and the police, petrified that the town's precious tourist trade would suffer.

'Speak nicely, Fitz. Remember who you are.' He remembered his mother often said these words to him, but the silly cow never told him who he was. He doubted she really knew for certain. But he did remember those occasions when, in her posh voice, she always managed to con some extra time out of the old biddy from whom they rented two poxy rooms, or some cash from the old fools whose flats she sometimes cleaned. But she never complained to the teachers when he told her of the way the kids used to taunt him because of his funny name. 'Fitzee, Fritzee, Mitzee got big titzees, is a shitzee'. They could keep that up the whole of break. When he couldn't stand it any longer he would lie on the ground on his side and curl himself up as small as he could until the bell went.

As he grew to young adulthood Fitz often marvelled at his own success, his know-how, his superiority over the rest of the rejects. He knew he would not have to endure their company for much longer. One day, he was certain, he would leave them behind forever. One afternoon as he occupied his favourite begging pitch, squatting against the wall of the County Museum, he gazed at the face of Judge Jeffreys on the sign above the restaurant on the opposite side of the road. This was the monster who had, it was said, cruelly prosecuted those honest Dorset men who had so bravely supported the Duke of Monmouth in his valiant effort to rid England of a cruel tyrant, his uncle King James II. How the kids in class soaked up the stupid teacher's story – but Fitz had never bought it. Nothing would ever convince him that a rich young man – the son of a dead king, who had everything, titles, land and money – had risked it all. For what? The teacher had fumbled her answer. All she had set out to do was to entertain her class with a story about a handsome young man and a wicked uncle, some fighting and blood spilling and gory executions. After all, history was not her subject and she was only a supply teacher. So Fitz answered the question for himself. All Monmouth had to do when his father died was behave himself and stay out of trouble, and learn how to get on with his uncle, the new king. Monmouth was not a hero – he was a stupid tosser. And so were all those losers who joined him after he landed at Lyme Regis on the start of his march to topple the King. Fitz thought that he would have treated the rebels in exactly the same way as the Hanging Judge had done. They were all fools and deserved everything they got, none more than James Stupid Monmouth, who had run away after the battle and had been caught hiding in a ditch, was taken to London and had his head chopped off. Fitz knew that in Monmouth's situation he would never have taken risks. He would have done anything to continue living in style and comfort. One thing Fitz knew with absolute certainty was that when he had money he would never, ever, ever risk it, share it, divide it or gamble it. Ever.

As he sat on the seat the familiar anger and frustration surfaced. He knew he was upper class. He felt it in his bones. His mother knew it too and could have had her reasons for never naming his father. All the same, the stupid cow had robbed him of his rightful dues. By now he should be enjoying all the fine things in life – like all the other sons of the rich and titled. He had seen their photos in the newspapers, emerging from the smart night clubs, driving their Ferraris, shaking hands with royalty, playing polo, marrying beautiful women.

He needed to find his rotten father, but he did not know where to start.

From time to time Fitz had to make himself scarce and he would sleep rough in a small wood on the land surrounding an old manor house near Dorchester. The manor's only occupant was His Lordship, who, everyone in the area knew, was the only surviving son of the family that had once owned nearly half of Dorset. From his refuge in the woods Fitz had occasionally seen the old man being picked up by taxi and returning a short time afterwards, when the driver would help him carry in several carrier bags full of shopping from the local supermarkets. No visitors called, or local tradesmen. Fitz often wondered why His Lordship was living alone. He wondered why he had no family. Had he never married? Fitz let his mind make up stories which ended with himself being the illegitimate son.

His instinct told him he had the glimpse of an opportunity and he could not stop a buildup of excitement and anticipation which impelled him back to the woods, even when the weather turned much colder, to wait and watch. Something was telling him that his big break was about to happen.

The moment came within minutes of the ambulance's departure as the dark evening was setting in. Without knowing whether the old man was sick or dead, Fitz moved swiftly to break into the manor.

He lived there for the following week, each day exploring every room and every floor and every nook and cranny. He only moved in daylight, never put a light on nor lit a candle, never disturbing anything, living off the contents of the fridge and the pantry. The longer he stayed the more relaxed he became, the more at home he felt.

He rehearsed the meeting with the old man, reassuring him, helping him, winning his confidence and then, when he had tested his gullibility, he would reveal that he was the son that His Lordship never knew he had. And then Fitz would come into his own and there would be a very happy ending.

If the plan did not work out Fitz decided he would burn the manor house to the ground and the old man with it.

Of course he was unaware that he was being watched. And of course he had no means of listening in to the phone calls when members of the local squirearchy discussed how to deploy the age-old ways to deal with all who intruded and trespassed on their land and property.

So, feeling totally secure, he returned to his lodgings one freezing cold night to check that his small stash of stolen phones and credit cards was still intact and then he returned to the manor.

It might have been the effect of smoking a spliff as he walked back which made him careless. Whatever the cause, as he stepped onto the parking area in front of the main door he was blinded by the security lights, which he knew full well were activated whenever something moved in front of the house. He also knew they would go off after a couple of minutes, so he stood stock still, cursing his own carelessness. Then, from out of the shadows of the building four or five men stepped into the light and they were carrying their guns under their arms. A jeep pulled up, the driver got out and released four hounds from the back. The dogs bounded over to Fitz, barking excitedly, and one jumped up to put his paws on his chest.

'Stand very still! Do not move!' Fitz heard the command over the barking of the dogs – but he couldn't move anyway. His fear paralysed him. Then he saw that whiskey was being poured into plastic cups and the booze was being tossed back. He tried to find the words that would get him out of this situation.

'Hey guys, it's OK for me to be here. I'm his lordship's ...'

But his mouth was too dry to speak. His head was bursting with the blood pounding through his veins. Anyway, no-one would listen to him. They knew already what they were going to do. They were in no hurry. The whiskey was passed around until the bottle was empty and all the time they stared at him contemptuously.

The dogs were called in. One of them shouted, 'Bugger off, low-life scum. You've got three minutes – and then we're coming after you and when we do, you're dog-meat.'

'So long, Pal.'

'Cheerio, Chum.'

As he raced back up the long drive, Fitz could hear the men were cracking up at their witty jokes. Then he heard a gun being fired and the men began whooping and hollering and the hounds began baying. He crashed through the woods where the branches and thorns cut him to pieces. He jumped into the shallow, freezing stream and out the other side. He crossed many fields until, his heart and lungs bursting, he fell into a deep ditch at the bottom of which he rolled himself into a small ball … and slowly froze to death.

The men, who had never left the drive, loaded up the hounds into the jeep, finished off another bottle and, still relishing the good sport, went their separate ways.

Poppies – Rosanna Wilmott

On a Dorset cliff-top

Frances Colville

He stood – as he stood every day – closer to the cliff edge than he should have done. Dressed in his old gardening clothes he looked like a man who cared for nothing – which indeed was the truth, since the sudden death of his wife six months earlier. He toyed, as he always did, with the idea of jumping, of ending his misery with a silent whoop of satisfaction as he crashed on to the rocks below

It took seconds, minutes perhaps, for him to realise that the screaming he could hear wasn't inside his head. Roused from his misery he turned and saw a lone woman, a hundred yards or so further inland, shrieking with terror. For the first time in six months he found himself aware of another human being.

He hurried to her side, soothing and questioning, and learned that she had seen a grass snake – two, three feet long – next to her shoe. To reassure her, he hunted for it, but it had vanished into the undergrowth. Unable to think of any other means of calming her, and loathe to leave her alone in such a state, he offered her tea at the beach café.

She accepted, and as they descended the hill together, she, having watched for such a chance for many weeks, wondered if he would ever realise that even on such a lovely spring day it was far too early in the year for grass snakes.

Battered fish

Maya Pieris

Slithering, sinking down the shingle slope I see an uneven shadow line, a vague shading winding along the beach. Closer, and curiosity is roused. I pause at a point where it is broken – crouching down I see that it is a chain of fish: little fish, like pieces of foil, hundreds (perhaps thousands) lying individually, but jaggedly, in groups, some in clumps like un-wedged clay. I stand up, startled by the beauty of the scene, the strange delicacy of this watery epic. Ahead, behind – the silver slivers fringe the beach. I bend again and carefully touch a fish, unexpectedly dry, and trace the indentations, like metal hammered to the thinness of wafers.

By now the beach is being populated by more early walkers. I stand up, walk on with the dog, who is surprisingly indifferent to the scene. The gulls are up, spinning crazily as the morning air takes them. A few bob serenely on the gently lapping water.

I still seem to be the only one to have noticed the scene. We walk slowly alongside the silver trail. I am fascinated and enchanted by the simple, fragile beauty before me.

It occurs to me suddenly that I should capture the scene, but the damn camera won't 'point and shoot'. My frustration is intense and immediate – now others have noticed and are recording this free exhibition for posterity. Desperation makes me consider asking someone to post me a copy or even email one, but I try to pretend that the moment is enough.

We continue walking on, the dog, nose to ground, more concerned to explore picnic litter. The chain continues its gentle undulation along the shingle, barely a break in the scaly links. I pause, squinting against the sun's haze, then we turn back from this mythical, mystical scene, silver fish wrought from moonlight and cast back to land.

Four days in June
Janet Gogerty

Patchwork; a cliché, but the view of Dorset from the car window was of rolling patchwork hills, every shade of green, dotted with darker circles of trees.

Kimberly had not left London since arriving three months earlier; replacing the flat ochres and golds of the Western Australian wheat belt with green parks and impossibly busy streets.

She had found Gavin on the internet; they were the same age and shared a great aunt. He was not as she had imagined.

'So you haven't seen the sea yet, Kimberly?'

'I didn't bring my bathers.'

'I'm not suggesting we go in, too cold, but the Jurassic coastline is amazing.'

He longed to plunge into the cleansing, chill sea, but he could not let her see the tattoos. She wasn't the sun-tanned independent Aussie he had pictured; quiet, a girl to ask out, if she wasn't a relative, if his life had been simple.

Tracing family had not been top of the agenda for her working holiday and Kimberly was nervous about this trip to the village where her grandfather was born. Why had she agreed to go with a man she'd never met? He was tanned, hard, but his eyes were kind.

'Gavin, how come you've never met Great Aunty Dot?'

'I've never met my father, let alone his relatives.'

'Sorry.'

'Don't be, Mum's family are lovely, I've got a great step-dad.' A step-father he was about to hurt. 'What brought you to England, have you got plans?'

'No plans, but I love London; nobody cares who you are or what you were doing back home.' She gazed out at the landscape, so much green in a tiny, overpopulated kingdom. 'Drought in Britain is a dry spring, if they could see our land ….'

'Ah … West Bay, our picnic stop.'

They parked by the harbour and looked across at the layered orange cliff. 'Looks easy,' said Gavin.

The climb wasn't high, but it was steep, the track had red footholds worn by other feet; one slip and she could roll down swiftly. She stopped to tie her jacket round her waist; clothing in England had to be rearranged continually.

At the top Gavin laid his jacket on a grassy mound near the edge.

Kimberly patted the velvet green in wonder. 'I thought the English seaside would be all flat pebbly beaches.'

As she watched him demolish the picnic, she asked what the plans were.

'I've booked a bed and breakfast for tonight. Aunty's expecting us tomorrow afternoon; then we can play it by ear. We don't want to put the old girl to any trouble.'

He had a tent in the boot. Honeysuckle Farm, there was sure to be a spare field he could camp in; he would see her safely back on the train to London first.

Kimberly was still crunching an apple when she felt a spot of rain. 'The sun's rays travel zillions of miles, then one fluffy grey cloud blots them out.'

They clambered down the hill; a heavy shower caught them before they reached the car.

'Charmouth, historic village and gateway to the Jurassic Coast,' Kimberly read the sign, '… and the sun's come out again.'

Standing on a beach of large pebbles, they viewed the green cliffs that sloped and fell along the coastline. He was enjoying her company, she saw through a fresh pair of eyes.

'The Earth's plates shifted and pushed the land up sideways, that's all I remember from geography.'

She followed him up the grassy slope, past warnings of coastal path closures. They stood on cracked fields that gently descended to the sea; even the diversion had slipped.

'Are you sure we're allowed here?'

The safest ground he'd stood on for months.

'Yes … geography lesson, England is shrinking.'

A muddy, wooded path felt safer and they emerged to see the sun sparkling on the waves far below. Her cousin marched on.

'I thought we were stopping here?'

'Let's see what's round the corner.'

'A Lost World,' Kimberly marvelled, as they looked down into a dense, green, wooded valley, where the cliff had slipped years before. 'If you fell down the cliff, no one would ever know.'

A secret, soft green that would enclose you, spare your family.

'If you jumped off, no one would know,' he said.

'Gavin, don't be so gloomy. Shall I peer over the edge?'

'No!' he felt suddenly giddy and grabbed her.

She was soft and trusting, he should be looking after her, not using her to reassure the old lady when they turned up on her doorstep.

Kimberly was used to flat paddocks stretching endlessly; the drop beneath the grassy edge made her stomach plummet. She was glad to be pulled back, held for a moment. He felt warm and strong, not like a cousin should feel.

Back on the road they drove through dappled green tunnels, trees arching over sunken roads; emerged to sunlit fields dotted with white shorn sheep and chestnut cows.

'Our B&B's the other side of town – historic Lyme Regis.'

She winced as they dove up a steep road and squeezed past a bus. The sun disappeared and they ascended into thick mist.

'Are you sure this is it?'

In answer, the door swung open and a middle-aged couple greeted them. 'Oh, when you said the lady would like the best room, I thought you were bringing your mother.'

Kimberly's room had a sofa and en suite bathroom. Gavin knocked to see how she was getting on.

'Beats my room at the house-share.'

'My attic room is like a house-share.'

'You can chill out down here, let's watch television.'

'Okay; seven o'clock we'll go into town and find that fish restaurant.'

He fell asleep on the sofa, it had been an early start. Rain beat on the windows; Kimberly curled up on the bed with extra jumpers.

After dinner she was surprised people were strolling around in the drizzle. Gavin wanted her to see the Cobb. Grey waves pounded the stone walls circling the harbour. He held her hand to climb the steps, but the wall, slippery with rain, sloped towards the sea. Kimberly begged to come down.

Along the sea front she admired pink and blue cottages adorned with wrought iron; they found bright yellow houses with green windows and doors.

'Everything is so cute. We must come in the morning and see those galleries.'

In the morning it was still misty; they trekked down a muddy field, dodging cowpats.

'Are you sure this is the shortcut to the beach?' asked Kimberly.

Descending through a wood they emerged to blue skies. Children played on the sandy beach sheltered by the Cobb and people sat outside their beach huts. The holiday atmosphere made them reluctant to leave.

To him the place was a toy town, full of dolls' houses … but what was real? He wasn't sure any more. She leaned up and kissed his cheek, the lightest of touches, but he felt his eyes prick. Was that how it started, a breakdown, like Mathew?

'Thanks, Gav, I'm having a lovely time.'

The kiss surprised her as much as him; did he feel the same way? She couldn't read his expression, he had told her so little about himself.

Aunty Dot's village was perfect; thatched cottages and gardens overflowing with flowers. At 'Honeysuckle Farm' they parked in a muddy lane. A middle-aged man opened the door suspiciously.

'Oh, sorry, we must have the wrong house.'

'Is that them, Brian?' a woman's voice came from inside.

Cautiously he ushered them in. Flowery settees and wooden dressers were nowhere to be seen. Everything was bright and modern, a computer desk tucked into the corner. Aunty Dot was sprightly, with rosy cheeks; Kimberly could see the seven-year-old girl who once skipped through fields.

'Welcome, dears. This is Brian, our neighbourhood watch co-ordinator and my good friend.'

'I haven't been down here long,' said Brian. 'Dot is one of the few originals. I fell in love with the village, now I run my business from home.'

The old lady took down a black and white photo.

'Uncanny, as soon as you walked in the door I saw the likeness; my sister, taken just before she left for Canada to marry her young man. You must have her adventurous spirit ...'

'... and Gavin; my nephew was a bad lot, we never knew you existed. Brian was worried you might be an impostor, but you've got the family eyes. My brother would have loved a grandson.'

Gavin felt uncomfortable under Brian's gaze, he must have guessed.

'What are your plans?'

Who was this Brian person? Did he think they'd take advantage of Aunty Dot; she seemed perfectly capable of looking after herself.

'Not sure yet, we're both flexible.'

'Oh you mustn't go yet, we've hardly got to know you,' exclaimed Dot, 'and you haven't met Amy. They're in Dorchester today, she's having her final check-up at the hospital.'

'Oh dear, has she been ill?' said Kimberly, 'and who is Amy?'

'Another great niece. She and her "partner" Sam live in a yurt in Brian's field. They're having a homebirth. We haven't had a baby in the village for ages.'

Gavin's plan to camp anonymously in a field seemed doomed. If Brian asked, he was on leave; he still had two days to decide.

'Tell us about your farm, Kim dear.'

'East of the Great Southern Highway, we haven't had enough rain for years.' She turned to Brian. 'Granddad married into a farming family.'

'We come from generations of tough country folk,' added Dot. 'Our family worked the land, but never owned it, that's why he left. What do you do, Gavin?'

'This and that.'

'I feel sorry for young people,' said their aunt. 'No job's secure and how anyone affords a house ... I admire what Amy and Sam are doing. I was like Gavin, couldn't decide, envied the older ones who had been away during the war.'

'What did you do?'

'Stayed here, started working for the local doctor, then his son ... I wanted to buy a retirement flat in Bridport, but I can't sell this cottage; when buyers do a survey they run a mile, it's made of branches and mud.'

Brian took them to the window and pointed up the hill, a roof glistened in the sun.

'Solar panels; barn conversion, everything ecologically friendly; plenty of room if you want to stay a few nights. Amy and Sam stayed all winter, the yurt lost its appeal in the snow.'

Kimberly hesitated; if she stayed they would want to know more.

'We mustn't keep you, Brian,' said Dot, as they finished afternoon tea.

Only the chocolate box village and the delicious cake fitted Kimberly's picture of how this day would be.

'Dear Brian knows how to take a hint; one advantage of being old is saying what you like. Now, what brings you two lost souls here? Only known each other two days, but you seem close, kissing cousins, nothing wrong with that.'

Kimberly blushed. 'I'm not adventurous; they packed me off to get away. Mum and Dad are on the point of walking off the farm, the land's worthless without rain, our neighbour committed suicide. Generations of farmers and all that's left is me and hundreds of acres of dust. Granddad didn't want you to know.'

'… and do you think that would be the worst thing that's ever happened to him?' She looked directly at Gavin. 'Kimberly's uncle was killed in Vietnam.'

She knew. He felt cold to the core; to break down in front of a girl and an old lady would be unbearable. Was this what it was like for Mathew? Invincible when they were over there, but back home ….

'You didn't get a tan like that in England. Why the secrecy? You should be proud,' said the old lady.

'My stepfather is very proud, especially the medal; he won't be when he knows I've gone AWOL.'

Low tide at Portland Bill – Sarah Gilpin

Too loved to say goodbye

Jeanette Lowe

Their last sight of Amelia was knee-deep in the millstream with her skirt tucked into her waistband, trying to coax a chicken out of the tree.

The fox had come in the night.

'We didn't hear a thing,' said Donna at breakfast that morning.

Amelia brought in their tea and toast, telling the full story in bits, two dead on the grass, three more vanished, one pecking at its corn as if nothing had happened, and the last one up the tree.

Donna looked out of the French doors into the fresh bright garden. There was so much life out there, so much dead dark wood in here. She looked at the other table, set up for two. She took in the photos along the mantelpiece. A young man stared out from several of them, a teenager, no more. She hadn't noticed him yesterday. He looked as if he didn't belong, as if he was uncomfortable in the pictures and wanted to climb out.

Rich followed her eyes. 'Wonder who he is?'

'He looks a bit like – *her*,' whispered Donna. 'I wonder if it was him. You know, yesterday.'

Rich swallowed a mouthful of toast. 'Don't whisper. People know you're talking about them if you whisper.' He looked at the pictures again. 'He reminds me of me, when I was about sixteen. I think it's his ears.'

Donna peered at his ears. Amelia came in to take away the cereal bowls.

'Why don't you keep them locked up in a hutch at night?' asked Donna.

Amelia stared at her, the single line between her forehead deepening. 'It's never happened before. I've never needed to lock them up. Not in twenty-three years.'

Inwardly, Donna tightened. Amelia had said that about their room: 'You won't need to lock your door. It's not London.'

They had unpacked quickly that first evening of their two-night stay. Most of their clothing was walking gear – rolled up T-shirts and thick socks and fleeces – and they left it in their cases. They had made tea – Rich went down to ask for milk, she didn't approve of those little pots of UHT – and washed their faces and hands and slipped on their flip-flops and got ready to leave for the local Indian.

They stood outside the bedroom door in the corridor.

'It seems a bit odd, not locking it,' said Donna.

'It wouldn't hurt to lock it,' said Rich.

'We'd have to ask her. She said she only had one key.'

'Yeah, right.' He turned. 'Come on, I'm starving, we've done twelve miles today.'

She followed him downstairs. 'God, wasn't it amazing? That blue, blue sea, it took my breath away.'

'I think it's only about nine miles tomorrow. If we make an early start we should have time for a nap before dinner.'

The Indian was fine, they shared chicken dopiaza, beef madras and cold beer. There was still light in the sky as they dawdled back, hand in hand. The tarmac gave way to a gravel path and they turned into the bed and breakfast.

They crept in through the back door. The house was dusky but they could just about see their way. There was a murmur from a television and Donna pictured Amelia stretched out on the sofa with her eyes shut. She led the way upstairs and past the two other letting rooms, opened their door and switched on the light.

Donna adjusted her eyes to the brightness. 'What's that?' she said.

'What's what?'

'That. On the bed.' She stepped towards it.

Rich followed her in. He reached out and touched it, cautious, as if it might be alive.

'You know what it looks like? It looks like an urn. You know, with ashes in,' said Donna.

'That's ridiculous.'

She curled her fingers around the silver body. The urn was plain, there was no detailing or engraving. She felt the life of it, she fought to keep her fingertips steady. Then she picked it up and shook it. 'There's something inside. Listen.'

He tugged it out of her hand and began to unscrew the lid. The tension in his face travelled down his slender arms to his fingers. They gripped tightly, every muscle finely shaped and honed and focused on making the lid move.

'Rich, *don't*,' said Donna. 'We *mustn't*.'

At last it came loose and he peered inside. 'Yup. Ashes. It's a dead person.'

Donna stepped away. 'It might be a pet. A dog.'

'That's a lot of ash for a poodle.'

He screwed it up again and put it on the bedside table. They sat down on the duvet, side by side.

'This is mad,' said Rich. 'Someone's been in our room and left a dead person on the bed. Told you we should have locked it.'

'If it was her, it wouldn't matter. She'd keep a spare key.'

They sat under the white-shaded bulb while darkness fell outside, staring at the silver urn.

'We'll have to ask her,' said Rich.

'It might not have been her.'

'You're saying another guest crept into our room and left the remains of

Uncle Max on the bed? And look – the tea cups are clean.'

'You're right, we'll have to talk to her.'

'Right.' He picked up the urn and made for the door. She followed him down and he switched on the light. Donna took a step towards the door marked 'Private'. She paused to listen to the murmuring TV. Then she tapped, so faintly she suspected Amelia wouldn't hear.

In moments Amelia was peering through the crack, frowning into the light. 'Hi – everything okay?'

'We found this,' said Rich, 'in our room.'

Amelia looked at his hands, her eyes empty. 'What is it?'

No one said anything. Amelia pushed the door open wide and reached out and touched the polished silver.

'How did it get in our room?' said Rich.

Amelia began to shake her head. 'I've no idea.'

'But who could have put it there?' said Donna.

'Are you sure it was in your room?'

Rich raised his shoulders two inches. 'We've just come back from dinner and found this on our bed. Someone's been into our room and left it there.'

Donna pointed up the stairs. 'Right there, in the middle of the bed.'

Amelia was still looking at it, not at them, but at the silver pot reflecting the glare from the hallway light. 'But what is it?'

Donna spoke firmly. 'It's an urn. It's someone's ashes.'

'Someone's ashes? Are you sure? How on earth did it get in your room?'

Rich sighed. 'This is getting us nowhere. We'll sort it out in the morning.'

They went back upstairs and the door clicked below.

'I can't sleep with that in the room,' said Donna.

'I'll put it in the bath.'

Donna stared at the dent where the urn had nestled, as if her gaze might make it disappear. Rich came out of the bathroom and she went in to brush her teeth. He had pulled the shower curtain across the bath. When she'd finished she turned off the light and got into bed.

Daybreak was bright. Donna woke sooner than she would have liked. Rich was snoring and she went to the toilet, saw the closed shower curtain and remembered.

She pulled it back. It sat there, perched in the middle of the bath. She took it out and put it on the floor by the toilet and stepped into the shower. When she came out of the bathroom wrapped in a towel, Rich was stirring.

'Hi, hon,' she said. 'Sleep well?'

'Great.' He sat up and stretched and looked across the room. 'What's that?'

'What?' said Donna. 'What?'

She looked to where he was looking and went to pick up a small white envelope from the carpet by the door. There was nothing written on the front. 'Shall I open it?'

'Want me to?'

'No.' She slipped out a sheet of paper, staring at the firm blue hand.

'*He loved the sea. Say goodbye to him. I just can't do it.*'

'Jesus. Is she nuts?' said Rich.

'We don't know it was her.' There was a noise in the corridor. He threw back the duvet. 'Come on, let's get breakfast. See what the other guests look like.'

Good mornings were said. There was another couple sat at the window table, a bit older than them. She was wearing lipstick and he had on a freshly ironed shirt. They smiled easily, chatted and sipped their coffees and ordered their full English. They look innocent, thought Donna; intent on themselves.

Donna and Rich ate in silence. Amelia came in from time to time and said, 'Everything okay?'

When she took away their empty plates she asked, 'Walking far today?'

'Along the coast path, about nine miles,' said Rich.

'Taking your car?'

'We'll walk into town and get a taxi, then get another to pick us up. We always do that.'

She stood holding the plates. 'Good. That sounds perfect.' She waited a few seconds more. 'Forecast's good, in any case.'

Back in their room they laced up their boots. 'What shall we do? About ….' Donna nodded at the bathroom.

'She gave us no clue,' said Rich. 'She must be psychotic.'

'We don't know it was her.'

'Of course it was her.'

Donna fetched the urn and put it on the table by the TV. 'But then who is it?'

Rich looked at it. Then he put it in a plastic Tesco's bag and stuffed it into his rucksack.

'This doesn't seem right,' said Donna.

'Well, we could leave it somewhere. We could put it in another guest's room, like a birthday present nobody wants, just keep passing it on to someone else.'

'Rich?'

'What?'

'Do you think she chose us specially?'

'If she did, why wouldn't she just ask?'

'We'd say no.'

He didn't respond. They put on their backpacks, walked into town to the taxi rank and climbed into a cab. In no time they were at the coast.

They left the road and followed the trail to the shore. The cliffs melted away and a stony path took them down to the beach.

'What about here?' said Rich.

'Are we really going to do this?'

'It's just saying goodbye.' He trudged down to the shoreline and unscrewed the lid, then sprinkled the ashes into the froth. He looked out to sea awhile, then twisted the empty urn back into his rucksack. Donna stood beside him.

'What now?' said Donna.

'Let's walk.'

'Goodbye,' she said to the sea and followed him back up the path.

As predicted, they got back early to the bed and breakfast. They showered and dozed, curled up together on top of the duvet. In the evening they bought fish and chips and ate them sitting by the river.

They slept like babies. In the morning they went down to breakfast and found that a fox had been at the chickens.

After breakfast they rolled up their clothing and repacked their cases. Rich put them in the car and Donna paid the bill. Then she pretended she had forgotten something and went back up to the room.

The empty urn was sitting on the bedside table. Next to it was the envelope, with nothing on the front. She took out the slip of paper and wrote on the back: *We said goodbye. He's alright now.* Then she left.

'It might have been that kid on the mantelpiece,' said Rich as they accelerated away in the car. 'Maybe he died in an accident or something.'

Donna turned back and saw Amelia knee-deep in the millstream with her skirt tucked into her waistband, trying to coax her chicken out of the tree.

'Guess we'll never know,' said Donna.

'Up is down' river reflection, Blandford – Jessica Knight

Dusting off the memories

Gail Aldwin

Ridges of clay showing through the glaze, the coil pot sits centre-stage alongside the factory purchases from Poole. Brought home wrapped in tissue, my son presented it like a treasure. Using the feather duster, I flick away a cobweb and peer inside. The bullet-shaped belemnites cluster at the bottom and rattle as I tip them into my hand, dust falling as they scatter. Taking the largest piece I study the indents of the fossilised squid. It was Tommy's prize find, the first time we went fossil hunting in Lyme.

The wind lashed my cheeks and strands of untamed hair escaped from my scarf. I sheltered by the rocks, false-footed by the incline; I lost my nerve. But Tommy strode on, his eyes set with concentration. Each time he showed a specimen to the expert, his shoulders hunched with disappointment when the bearded man shook his head. Other fossil hunters in flapping raincoats scurried across the beach like crabs, picking and turning the pebbles. Screwed up with anticipation, Tommy continued the search, forcing over boulders too heavy to carry, fingering the stones like jewels beneath. When it was time to walk back, he stiffened, shoving his hands in his pockets, shrugging off the arm I placed around his shoulders. With his elbows sticking out like wings, he bent his head and studied the ground. The others wandered off, but I stayed and watched him, my face wet with drizzle. At a rock pool he dropped to his knees, the water like obscured glass, he ran a finger through the weeds and shells. Removing a cylinder of black stone, he ran along the shingle to catch up with the guide. Tommy's waving fist confirmed it was indeed a fossil.

Thoughts of the beach capture me, willing me to go to the sea. I hesitate as the memories spin; my toes curl inside my slippers. If only Tommy were here, we'd be off and away, the rain no deterrent. But the boy's long gone, grown into a man and rarely home for a visit. I return the coil pot to its place on the mantelpiece and trace the lines of clay that my son once rolled. I think about the boy, his white-blonde hair and his face lengthens as I picture the man. Always on a Sunday he phones and asks me what I'm doing. This week I'll tell him I'm dusting, dusting off the memories.

Liberation song 2001

Phil Mullane

The blue mug strikes the plate
A dull clank
Like a dull, dead bell.

5 am
The cat's bed is empty
The apricot rose has lost its scent
The last apple, small and hard, fails to tempt me.

Kabul has fallen to the BBC!
A trio of Taliban sympathisers,
Roped together like a three-headed beast,
Is marched away from the camera's eye
Through a crumbling gateway to a certain death.
A child plays with a kite on a dusty street
Cutting a pattern from the mindless sky.

Outside
A lonely robin rings out
Its sweet-sweet wake-up call
Upon the morning air.

The box
Patrick O'Neill

I scramble in panic for a moment, but then my fingers pass over it. The key is there in the brickwork, just as it should be. And now it is time.

Charles,

By now you will be sitting in your armchair by the fireplace and will have spent long minutes staring into the flames. You will have Scotch, neat on ice, beside you, and will have opened your newspaper only to find this unexpected note fall from within.

I hope you are sitting comfortably.

How clever you have been, to hide it for such a length of time – for so many years. You must be enormously satisfied to have concealed it all so effectively. I can only imagine the planning and attention to detail that must have been involved. Eliminating all risk, covering every base; like a twisted extension of your work life; underwriting the perfect insurance policy, watertight and without flaw.

From the clockwork, suffocating machine that you have created for our lives, I never would have guessed it. Pathetic really, that I have been so easily hoodwinked and manoeuvred; no more than an object being shifted from one place to another in this particular compartment of your life.

But how many other compartments are there, Charles, other than those which I have now discovered?

Yes, you have hidden it neatly – just like the key lodged in the brickwork outside the front door; the one you always leave for me on Tuesday night when I return from Horticulture class. The one I will use to open the door with, in one hour.

Our son will be with me and you know why. I have seen the bruises, and the burns over the years; strange that I have never witnessed them being inflicted though. Just another compartment, tightly closed, only opened when the correct conditions come into play. How ugly you have become, Charles; how very far from the man I thought you would develop into, all those years ago at the church.

I cannot help finding humour in it though, that, after such careful planning, such immaculate, intricate track covering, all should finally be exposed by Sam.

Maybe he is not so stupid, after all, as you would like to have it. I see how he cowers in your presence, tail between legs.

Dogs are stupid, Charles, but they do not forget. Perhaps as he whimpered and scrabbled at the floorboards in the office room, Sam was seeking his own revenge by ripping the lid from your most treasured compartment; the one you wanted buried forever, in the darkest recess of our home.

And what an ingenious place to hide it, under the rug, far beneath the floorboards. Your little wooden box of memories. On some level you must have known it was a mistake – the flaw to the perfect policy – but you could not resist, could you? You could not resist the pleasures it would bring again and again.

I have often wondered what thoughts fill your mind as you watch the dancing light in the evenings. I have seen the strange glimmer in your eyes when you gaze into the crackling embers. Your eyes are dark, but in those moments – despite the reflections of the firelight – they seem blacker still. Yes, I have wondered what fills your mind, but now that I know, I wish I did not.

Lifting the boards was simple, even though you had bent nails here and there to make it seem impossible. All I needed to do then was reach into the darkness and lift your secret world into the light. Wrapping the box in old gorse only made me more curious.

It took but a screwdriver to lever-off the latches behind the padlock and break the seal.

To begin with, it was the smell that took me off guard, as you can imagine.

Lifting out each object within the box was difficult for me, Charles. I will admit to leaving the office room, more than once, to vomit in the toilet off the corridor. I tell you that not to make you feel empowered or dominant, as you would like it to be, but because I need you to understand how far apart our realities are. Your pleasures are simply my disgust.

Each time I was sick though, and thought I could not continue, I found strength to return and finish what I had begun, to see everything within the box. In the end maybe I was wrong, but there is no benefit to knowing half a secret. The imaginings are always worse than the truth, or so I am told.

The ring was first, resting on black leather. I held it to the light for a long time, trying to make out the initials inscribed into its golden underside: JM. It meant something, but I could not place it.

But as I lifted the next object, the understanding was sudden and overwhelming. Blackened and shrivelled though it was, I recognised it as a human finger from the bright red nail polish.

I have thought of it since; of how swiftly the complete picture emerged, Polaroid-like, before me. I did not even need to read the neatly cut newspaper clippings at the bottom of the box to confirm it. Somewhere, the idea must have already been there.

Maybe I had simply not wanted to see it.

JM: July Mathews.

She was the first, wasn't she, Charles? And who could forget, with all the coverage that came afterwards, day after day, her young face staring from the front pages.

There are words for people like you, Charles, but none that could adequately portray the reality. Strange, isn't it, that when no one understands a problem they pigeonhole it – give it a name – as though that may solve it. But it does not work; the name is only a tag – no more than a label, easily peeled away – a weak attempt to feign understanding of that which cannot be understood. I wonder how you see your label, Charles; how it makes you feel. Serial killer.

A young prostitute disappearing from Oxford's Gloucester Green in the height of summer wasn't exactly news, but when others started to vanish – well – that was when the real interest – the real fear – began, was it not?

How you must have loved it. What is it, five years now? A long time, Charles.

And how exhilarated you must have been when they began to discover the bodies in the woods at Sulham and when the autopsies revealed what the girls had suffered.

What made you choose Sulham? Was it that we used to walk there with Sam and you had come to know it well? Or was it because of the other stories, the legends of Sulham Woods; the rumours of witchcraft and Satanism being rife in the area. You must have known that the bodies being discovered there would create more fear, more beautiful mystery around what you had done.

73

The newspapers cherished it, of course; the bodies finally being located in remote woodland steeped in rural mythology, at the very centre of Berkshire's green belt.

Yes, in the very acreage favoured by Senior Consultants at the Royal Berkshire Hospital to set up home, a new legend was born, the Surgeon of Sulham.

How powerful you must have felt: the Surgeon of Sulham, always one step beyond the authorities; that most feared of predators: the killer that is not satisfied with death alone but seeks to witness suffering, however long it may take.

In amongst the dried bones and ears was the black leather mask; the one that the girls must have seen: the Surgeon's mask. It must have been too tight and could barely have covered your face. The way you had roughly cut the eyes from the leather was unlike you too. I would have expected something neater, somehow. But then maybe you had conjured the Surgeon as an image of everything you secretly craved; the alter ego you longed to be: the monster without conscience, disconnected from conformity and the neat, well-heeled Charles that you presented to the world each day. Yes, I see that now: Charles Latham, the quiet underwriter, minimising risk at every turn, becoming the Surgeon: the wild risk-taker, prescribing and administering the ultimate medicine: mutilation without anaesthesia.

How did it feel, Charles, in the dead of night, in the woods, as they screamed for mercy whilst you knelt over them with the scalpel? Did it make you feel powerful, superior, to have such control? You have attempted to introduce such command to our bedroom at times but I have always rejected you. I wonder now if I had permitted it, whether those seven girls might still be alive.

The box was a mistake, but how could you resist collecting the trophies that would let you re-live the events as your fingers brushed across them. Yes, Sam found it, but he would not have found it had it not been placed there. Either way, the control is lost. I now decide your fate, as you decided theirs. I choose whether to inform the police or to bury it again beneath the floorboards as you have done.

But you made another mistake too – an oversight within the organised compartment that is our home life.

It runs like clockwork, and Tuesday is no different: you come home, not late, and after you have hidden the key in the brickwork outside the front door for me, you align your black brogues – military style – in the porch. You eat the lasagne that is always left warming for you in the oven; then the Scotch, neat over ice; the armchair; the fire watching and, finally, the newspaper.

How was the lasagne, Charles? Deadly Nightshade berries were commonly used in the practice of witchcraft. They are plentiful in the churchyard amongst the brambles. It won't be long now.

I have read that *Atropa belladonna* causes severe stomach cramps and bleeding from the eyes before death. There will be convulsions and organ failure.

I'll bury you at Sulham, in the woods. When they find you they may even blame it on the Surgeon.

No longer yours,
Mary-Anne.

The house is silent. Not the usual silence that fills Church Farm House, but a heavy, expectant silence.

In the porch, Charles' brogues are neatly aligned. It is cold outside and I have left Jack in the car. There are some things a ten-year-old should not see.

The living room glows in the light of the fire, which crackles and hisses angrily into the quiet. Outside, the bell of St Peter's tolls the hour across the fields.

Charles' high-backed chair faces the fire, away from me, guarding my view of his body. I do see his arm though, twisted strangely and laying motionless over the armrest. His whisky tumbler lies smashed on the flags of the hearth.

I take a step closer but then freeze as I hear the voice, strangely muffled, from the fireside.

'I always check the box before I eat on a Tuesday.'

I try to take a step backwards, towards the kitchen, but my legs will not obey.

'I gave the lasagne to Sam. I hope you don't mind.'

Then, as he stands, masked, naked, engorged, holding a scalpel, I stumble backwards to the kitchen.

'Charles … please, no.'

Something cold and thin runs across my neck. I look to the kitchen door. Jack is there, staring on at us. I reach my hands to him but the darkness is overwhelming.

Flaky Portland rock – Sarah Gilpin

The landslip

Karen Wright

It had begun as a fine mist of water clinging to Grey's waterproof and making it stick to her arms, but she was not conscious of the rain, even as it became more steady, driving into her body as she balanced precariously part way up the landslip.

Other fossil hunters had downed tools and were trudging back towards the car park, through the heavy shingle and cloying grey mud flows. Grey did not move because she could see a white, dense object, which water and her probing were slowly revealing.

As the sky darkened she had exposed a long bone with a bulbous socket extension.

'Found something?'

Grey almost fell backwards, but regaining her composure with the help of a small pick she was able to risk glancing down. His features were obscured by a cap, but, with his North Face anorak and binoculars, clearly a persistent birdwatcher.

'Yes, I think I have', she said, unable to hold a note of excitement from her voice.

'Can I help in any way?'

'Could you bring that chisel up to me?'

Painstakingly, Grey began to prise the bone from the debris into which it had fallen as Black Ven once again disgorged its secrets.

Suddenly, however, it became clear. This was not a Jurassic bone, nor could it be an animal femur.

'This shouldn't be here!' she gasped,

'And neither should you, you interfering bitch!'

Grey's axe fell again, this time mortally. Her blood washed down the beach to the sea.

Lady Caroline Pountney

Audrey Lee

Seven years old and knowing nothing, simply seeing, touching, loving ... living in the mystery, embracing and believing it, swept forwards, onwards, upwards. Seventy now, still knowing nothing, simply seeing, touching, loving ... quite resigned to mystery ... embracing and believing it ...

looking back, always back, remembering ...

In this residential home, sucked dry of blood, I look but do not see through glass and geriatric eyes. They tell me it is Worthing beach. It is remote, untouchable. It is a sham, a simulacrum. On Weymouth beach the sand was hot and real. On Weymouth beach I knew I was alive. I was significant enough for synchronicity ...

looking back, always back, remembering ...

On Weymouth beach when I was seven, splashing round the firm-ribbed bay in salty ribbons, eyes cast down for slipper shells, I saw a massive book half-buried in the silt – sodden, useless, tide-marked buff and brown, turning into sand and weed, its spine sea-changed for limpets, and on the random page that faced the sky all words obliterated save for three – in large black print – these three words spared until my gaze preserved them for a lifetime:

my surname, mine – my own, prefixed by 'Lady' and by 'Caroline'

I knew then all there is, is wrapped in mystery

Seven years old and knowing nothing, simply seeing, touching, loving ... living in the mystery, embracing and believing it, swept forwards, onwards, upwards. Seventy now, still knowing nothing, simply seeing, touching, loving ... quite resigned to mystery ... embracing and believing it ...

looking back, always back, remembering ...

give me the undiluted body smell of sand and seaweed, smell and stink of sand and seaweed, sexy, punch-drunk rude and vulgar, get-you-into-bed my lovely ... the sanitised oh-so-polite apologetic whiff of Worthing ... *don't forget that you're a lady, Caroline ...*

give me the harbour droppings, seagull splattered – nets and boats and wooden timbers – essences of cod and mackerel – fishermen intent on fishing, fishermen who frowned and shouted, photographic no-way-men ... blue, blue sea and blue, blue sky arcing into mystery ...

the *real* seaside, the salty smell, the body smell of sand and sea-weed where the three words waited for me ... and the gas-works, leaking gas, the gas that lighted up the hissing gas-lamps, the taper long and white and necessary lighting up the hissing gas, the key you could turn up or down and never up enough …

the milk delivered out of nowhere in an aluminium pail, a *real* milkman and a horse that slipped on ice and broke a leg ... how the milkman wept! I did not know which had been shot. The greenhouse made of milk-bottles, the chickens in the Anderson … trips to Portland and to Sandsfoot ...

running round the harbour wall to get to school with jumps that spanned the lottery of life – one slip would have been enough for an unlucky dip – the train you had to look out for, the train that ran on silver tracks along the ground in front of you or followed you deliberately from behind, the train your mum did not believe in ... a *real* train ... what luck there was a fisherman who bawled me out of danger ...

St Mary's dark sardine-stuffed classroom, an exercise in facing fear – anxiety rode high upon the crates of milk, the chalk and slates, the cardboard discs and raffia – rode high upon a pregnant teacher weeping for her wartime baby ... 'Pull yourself together,' someone said. 'Oh, peaceful England,' we all sang ...

'Here's my pencil – touch my willy,' James McFee, come to the front, leave her alone and don't be silly – chased over virgin ground by gangs of dirty boys shouting dirty words – discovering a new way home, a clean and secret way away from sticks and stones.

My Auntie Dora's house was by the gasworks. 'It is hard,' she said, 'to meet the right man after you have married the wrong one'. He called her his peach because she was one, a Peach. Her cheeks were pink and juicy. She used Woolworth's rouge.

Seven years old and knowing nothing, simply seeing, touching, loving ... living in the mystery, embracing and believing it, swept forwards, onwards, upwards. Seventy now, still knowing nothing, simply seeing, touching, loving ... quite resigned to mystery ... embracing and believing it ...

looking back, always back, remembering ...

'Suddenly everyone burst out singing' – vivid flashes, fireworks and celebrations. All along the front, in twos and threes and arm in arm – sailors still in uniform kissed giggling girls, handed out sweets, cocky by the red clock tower. 'Dead with heartache,' some of them, my mother said. Parties, parties, everywhere. Long tables dressed in white with cup-cakes, sandwiches ...

A little girl, my age, sitting on a step with hatred etched indelibly upon her face, a snapshot lodged inside my mind for over sixty years ...

Worthing beach is cold and lonely, a long way off from Weymouth sands. No words wait for me here. Lady Caroline Pountney dissolved in the sea along with my significance a long long time ago. Was she, am I, fact or fiction?

All my memories are wrapped in mystery.

Meaning runs away when it hears my feet approaching.

Hive Beach – Abbie Williams

The world from my window

Margery Hookings

Let me take you now to Lush Places, an enchanted village where the luvvies seldom venture, where the mist swirls around and around the top of Bluebell Hill like a maelstrom.

Just down the road is that well-heeled, genteel little Dorset town whose name all non-locals mispronounce.

'We love Bee-minster,' they say, their unintentional mistake instantly revealing that they are not of this county.

They don't see the bored youngsters on a Saturday night, the sad, drug-taking loser in a dirty flat, the lonely old lady living on her own, and the couple yelling at each other in front of their children and a blaring television.

'And we just love Bridport,' the incomers say. 'It's so arty, so Bohemian, so *cosmopolitan*.'

And as they venture through the artists' quarter, picking up pieces of distressed furniture for next to nothing but making a tidy profit for the dealers who bought it from Lawrences' auction, they find themselves in Waitrose where they buy figs and Parma ham and a bunch of flowers they could have got for half the price from the stall outside.

They wander along the street market, picking up pieces of junk and muttering that they used to have something like that and should never have got rid of it. They walk by the *Big Issue* seller and the man with the tattooed neck, the woman with a large behind who is wearing leggings and a snotty-faced child who still has a dummy at the age of four.

They don't see the shoplifter hovering around Frosts, the deals going on up narrow alleyways, or the mad woman made mad by the man who abused her.

Likewise, Lush Places does not appear on the incomers' radar. It ducks it, scrambles it or does whatever it needs to do to avoid detection. It limbos under the Beautiful Bar and if you ever find it, it will be purely by chance. And if you go back to try to discover it again, it won't be there, it will have disappeared.

While the sun beats down in upmarket Beaminster and glows along Bridport's South Street like a blazing spacehopper, Lush Places quietly gets on with everyday life, unhindered by tourists, the crowds and even the people who just want to get away from it all.

It is protected by a bubble of mist, and reveals itself only when it knows the incomers have gone home for the day, or are safely tucked up in their boutique hotel beds and quaint B&Bs.

This is the place where I live, the place I love, where three-legged cats go hunting at night, gutted rabbits are left as gifts by a gamekeeper in the morning and an unhealthy interest is taken by the neighbours in other people's recycling.

It's where when my washing machine and tumble dryer break down, I can rely on a neighbour to not only provide me with an alternative but to offer to do the ironing too.

It is a place where when a Londoner scrapes my car while doing a U-turn and then says *that kind of thing happens all the time in Highgate,* I can be sure that three people have clocked his registration number and a fourth will offer to rearrange his kneecaps.

It is a place where when I fall off my bike into a hedge after too many drinks at a party down the road, a passing policeman tells my husband who is cycling ahead that he has just seen me crash, but can't stop to help because he's looking for poachers.

It's a place where we take direct action against obtrusive street lighting, which pokes its beams into our bedrooms in the name of Dorset County Council improvements, by getting licensed deer stalker Mr Champagne-Charlie to take each one out, individually, with a well-aimed rifle.

It's a place where the drinkers keep on drinking, yet the publican doesn't have enough trade to keep him afloat. It's a place where the Jehovah's Witnesses arrive en masse, determined to shake up this godless place once and for all.

It's the place where when a door-to-door salesman makes an unwanted call on an elderly neighbour, the village folk step in and direct him to Beaminster. Where when a man trips over the kerb, six arms reach out to break his fall.

I see a lot of things.

From here, I catch a glimpse of the tall, tall beech trees on Bluebell Hill, the indentation to the west caused by an aeroplane that crashed in the war. Across to the right is the flat-topped summit that up until a few years ago was always considered the highest point in Dorset until the Ordnance Survey revised its maps.

Opposite my window is the village green named in memory of two young men lost in battle. And at the shop, now threatened with closure, is a union flag, flapping defiantly as the tractors and their loads of potatoes trundle past.

You can hear the children playing in the school yard, the electronic bell clanging, calling them to come back inside. And up on the allotments, a man is leaning on a hoe while a tramp strolls by, trying all the doors as he glides past and on up to the Christian retreat on the hill.

And the ancient stone church, mellow in the autumn sun, reverberates to the words of a long-dead parson who was famous for his sermons: *Charity begins at home … but it should not end there.*

This is the place I love. A million miles away.

Let me take you back ten years to how this love affair began. I am climbing up a narrow staircase and looking out of a bedroom window. A village square, with a red telephone box, an old water pump, a corner shop, a pub and a village green. It is peaceful, quiet. I watch as the paper-boy props his bike up against the kerb and ambles, ape-like, into the shop. In headphone oblivion, he does not hear the crash when the bike tips into the road.

The driver of the Land Rover that comes tearing around the corner doesn't see the bike either. There is a metallic scrunching sound and a crowd appears from nowhere. In unison, people emerge from their front doors, put their hands over their mouths and then scratch their heads. An old man with a beard prods the mangled bicycle with the hooked end of a curly walking stick and tries to retrieve it from the Land Rover's undercarriage. Another man with a twirly pipe hanging from his mouth grabs the handlebars to try to pull the bike out.

The Land Rover driver shrugs, goes into the shop to get *The Daily Mail*, comes back out again and gets behind the wheel. He starts the engine, disengages the handbrake and, with a crunch, the Land Rover wheels go up and then over the bike, which is taken along for the ride like a modern art version of bull bars.

The paper-boy comes out of the shop with a bag of sweets, mounts a non-existent bike and gets five yards down the road before realising it isn't there.

The *Londis* sign creaks above the shop. And then a ginger wig rolls by like tumbleweed as the church clock strikes thirteen.

From the warmth of the room, I feel a hand on my shoulder.

Mr Grigg.

'What do you think?' he says, as I gaze out of the window. 'Do you think we should buy it?'

The estate agent is hovering behind him, particulars in his hand.

'Does madam like the house?'

'I'm sold,' I tell him.

Circle song

Judy Hall

Come gentle stranger and hear my tale. It is seldom that I have the chance to speak. Yes, by all means, light a fire although the warmth no longer reaches my old bones. I am Belagh of the Brigantians, keeper of this ancient Purbeck land.

The womb of shining water lies quiescent now, cradled in the encircling stones. Those that remain, that is. So much desecration has there been. The great avenue is gone and forgotten. But it was not always so. This was a sacred space poised between the worlds as I now hover between life and death, circle and hill. Above, on the great green down, the warrior kings lie silent in the nine barrows, their peace undisturbed.

For more than a thousand years my beloved and I tended these holy places with ritual and reverence. When the first invaders came, we made the circle invisible, hidden amongst inky trees. Camping briefly on the place between the hills, they sent scouts to the top of the Creech. But the barrow wights did their work and soon silence mantled the valley again. For another thousand years we rested. More invaders came, building a castle on the saddle between the hills. Centuries passed but their church did not disturb us. We lived in harmony and respect.

But then, the puritanical ones came. The invader's religion had quietly honoured the sacred sites, this one did not. These were hard-faced men, shaven-headed, muttering darkly as they cast down painted statues from the church with pikes and pick-staffs whilst others whitewashed the pictures from the walls.

When they took the castle, we hoped it would suffice, but no. On May Day they came, sniffing after the maidens who slid secretly to the place of the Mother's shining womb. In the old days it was a time for rejoicing, music and song danced under the full moon. Many a child was conceived on that day. Now the celebration was furtive, banned by those sour old men who knew nothing of the joy the Mother could bring. From my place on the high down, I saw the torches come. I ran down the hill to warn the women. But it was too late. With loud cries, the encroaching men violated the sacred ground, urinating into the Mother's womb. With great branches they levered the ancient stones from their resting place, toppling them. Stones groaned as they shattered and split. The earth shrieked, heaving as though to throw off these heretical invaders.

Raising my staff, I stepped into the circle. Seeing my blue woad and hairy frame, they shrank back. Then fell on me. The leader, a grim grey man, shrieked:

'Begone foul fiend,' and thrust his torch at me.

I reached out to push it aside. Knocking my staff from my hand, he raised his holy book and struck my arm. Torch and book united in flame. A torrent of words enmeshed me, sent me staggering from the circle into the welcoming dark.

From without, helplessly I watched as my beloved was brought, stripped naked but clothed in light. Her beloved form was beautiful to me; it should not be defiled.

'Witch,' they screamed, 'Devil's harlot.'

One, taller and sterner than the rest, pronounced over her as he ducked her head into the pool. Surely he knew you cannot kill a woman who left her body three thousand years ago? But the grim grey man held her tight beneath the shining water while my long-dead heart thudded and faltered until I thought it would break forever. No matter how I strove, I could not pass through the invisible barrier that grim grey man had cast. I could not reach her.

When they lifted her out, Imraigh raised her head proudly as water streamed from raven tresses toward the earth. Outlined by the silver moon, she smiled gently at where I stood helpless in the outer dark.

'Witch, burn the witch,' the cry went round.

Wood was brought, fire lit. But it did not touch her. The men choked on acrid smoke, but my lady stood serene under the silver moon. Angrily, they dragged her away. With words she was banished from the circle. Bound into time. As she faded into the quiet woods, I moved towards her.

And the grim grey man pounced. Muttering his incantations, he forced me up the hill. But there I could call on the barrow wights for aid. Misty and silent, they hung wraithlike in his path. There was no need for them to speak. The icy coldness that oozed from their incorporeal forms was far stronger than words and his book held no sway here. He ran, shouting back over his shoulder that he would never rest until it was settled, he would banish me. I would be gone.

For four hundred years he stood between the castle and the church. As souls were called to their maker, he blocked the gateway. This was his army, his soldiers of Christ, his to command. Grey and bitter, he did not let go. His ghostly horde importuned the villagers:

'Set us free, for the love of God, set us free.'

But no one heard. A few felt the ghostly presences, shivered and shuddered before moving on, grew ill at ease. Dis-eased. Crops withered, animals passed quickly by. The castle walls fell.

The circle was all but buried, the shining lake grown stagnant and stale. On my hill, I watched. In her wood, my lady waited. And the grey man shouted imprecations that no one heard.

With the new millennium came change. People sickened and died, the visitors fell away. The village was uneasy, violence flared under the castle walls. People muttered at things glimpsed from the corner of a hastily averted eye. Cats spat with fur spikes raised. Dogs rumbled low in their throats as the dismal horde pressed close. I called again to the Mother for aid.

On Midsummer's Day the ley lines sang as though sensing a power great enough to free us. A bush on the Creech burst into flame, visible for miles. On the sacred lake ripples stirred. Was this to be the time?

Two women came. One, tall, grey haired but athletic, strode ahead. The other one, short, fat and out of condition, puffed her way up the Creech, flung upward with the aid of a force nine gale. Cushioned in a hollow below the top, the taller one patted her pockets. Out came a pendulum. The other held a golden crystal. Could it be, were they strong enough, would they see? Quietly they stood for a few moments, heads bowed, watching the pendulum swing wildly before their words rushed to me on the wind.

'Look, over by the church I can see a clergyman, grey and stern with a tall, wide-brimmed black hat. He's holding the gateway, trapping many souls. He's the one who has been causing all the misery. And over there on the barrows, there's an old man dressed only in blue woad. Seems like he's keeping a wary eye on us.'

'Hardly surprising, we don't know what to make of ourselves most of the time,' the dumpy one laughed. 'Can you open the gateway?'

'I've got to get past the clergyman first. Can you distract him for me?' She turned towards the church below.

The dumpy woman looked pensive for a moment and closed her eyes.

'He came with Cromwell's men when they took the castle. He says he had a job to do but he didn't realise it would take this long. I think he's ready to go now and if he leaves the others can follow. Get that portal open.'

The grey-haired woman twitched and shook, her mouth opening on an eerie sound. Above her head, a hole whirled open stretching down towards the church. And I saw the spirits leave. A multitude rising to the portal where, from billowing light, beckoning hands reached down to help them on their way, the grim grey man following behind.

'We'd better leave it open for now to be sure they've all gone. Let's take a look at the circle, see what's going on there.' The older woman gestured to the foot of my down.

'Imraigh, wake up, help is coming at last.' I called but my lady didn't stir, surely she must feel this but it had been so long. Impatiently I made my way down the track towards the circle but the invisible barrier bounced me back. The grey man may have gone, but his words still held their power.

Those strange, unearthly sounds shrieked out again, echoing all around. The tall woman stood in the circle, head thrown back. The ley lines opened, power radiating out. The circle was whole once more. The barrier before me fell away.

And here was the dumpy woman smiling and reaching out her hand, come to lead me back. She was calling Imraigh too, inviting her to reclaim the circle and regain the land. My lady stirred like a tree awakening from winter slumber. From high on the hill a raven flew to her shoulder and gladly they came to my side. At my feet was my staff of power, lost in that battle long ago. The ancient jewel at its tip shone with red fire. With it and my beloved, I was complete again.

Together the women poured water into the stagnant womb.

'Glastonbury water from Chalice Well,' they told us, 'to bring the Mother back. See, here is her statue set up in the centre. We honour her, and you.'

When it was done and the circle sang its power again, they left.

I took Imraigh in my arms. We had a ritual to perform, a magical, sacred act that would restore potency to the land. We lay together in the Mother's womb.

The circle closed. All will be reborn.

In the summerhouse shadows – Bronwen Coe

'Dead slow'

Bronwen Coe

The sea is so full today; a vessel filled to brimming, yet incomprehensibly it is held within the lip of the bowl's boundary walls and so stops here, tamely grazing at the shingle. A great puddle of mystery and unaccountability, defining its own jurisdiction in the seemingly flimsy line that arcs west and east.

Leashed, this English sea obediently confines itself within its completeness.

Twice a day and night, on an invisible in-breath it hauls itself down the beach. Twice a day and night, with a steady exhalation it returns. Nothing perturbs this feat of immemorial engineering.

Now here midweek, mid-afternoon, the sun is on, the heavens blue. There is the stillness and silence that fashion timelessness.

The jetty pokes itself out through the platter of water, both obtrusive and inconsequential, the mightiness and solidity of its manufactured and inscrutable concrete form dwarfed by the formless shifting softness of its oceanic neighbour. 'Dead Slow' the notice on the wall forbiddingly commands.

In the distance, huddled figures spatter the beach cradled by the golden toothy cliff that towers awkwardly behind them, a monolithic fortress, a blunt and static prow. A dog bounds ozone enthralled: soundless.

Along the promenade, ambling people arm in arm deliciously at ease, lazily patrolling the cusp of their secure and knowable world. The fabric of the still air soaked and imprinted (somehow not rent) by the disparate gulls' glissandi.

On the rocks that skirt the jetty a father and his small white-stick-legged son manoeuvre a route across the jumbled crags. Methodically the man prospects each stage of the route and then returns, takes the child's hands in his and guides him aloft to the next landing stage.

The gentle intensity of care and trust are palpable. Each brief separation gathered back into togetherness and safety. The father will remember these moments and store them proudly in the recesses of his paternal heart. Much later the boy, then a father himself, will also remember this idyllic window by the sea. For both, the special treasure shared, all differences reconcilable while time stands irrelevant and the sea here is nowhere different now and then.

Around the other side of the globe in another island country, another benign sea ... oh ... defies its possibilities, summoning the unconscious fiend, its latent beast to arise and surge.

Methodically regardless it lavishly devours its own awful quota. Whole towns: men, women, children in buildings, ships and vehicles all mere flotsam, a mobile battlefield of human debris that imprints its hideous memory with an unheeding ferocity.

Mortain Bridge, Blandford – Becky Hinsley

Isar Defoe

Jim Aldhouse

She stepped confidently onto the rolling walkway and began to negotiate the bands towards the faster centre lanes. Through the Kevlar she could see the Regent Street traffic 15 metres below her. London was full of tourists these days. The shops teeming, antique red hybrid buses puttered their way through town. She shifted the bag to her other hand for better balance, it was bulky but light. Already she was missing the serenity of the penthouse at Westminster Skies but she had a job to do. A job she wanted to do.

Erich Defoe had been her first civil partner. Successful film director and artist, he was one of few men who could afford her; she had chosen formal business wear, pinstripe, severe but at the same time powerfully feminine. The double-breasted short flared jacket was low cut at the bust to reveal her perfect silhouette; at first glance she appeared to be wearing very little underneath. The truth. Dressed to impress. Dressed to dominate.

She still had difficulties coming to terms with Erich's will. She had never heard of the woman she must meet to fulfil probate demands. The legal team had insisted on a signature to indicate the meeting had taken place, so she was on her way to Southwark Central to satisfy those conditions before they would release the capital. Erich had been very clear in his testament. There were things she had to take to this woman and it had to be said part of her was curious.

She thought she used to satisfy all of Erich's needs. It had been her first purpose after all. She downloaded all the recipes he ever mentioned, she trained to professional chef level, she satisfied all his sexual fantasies, even the ones which required another partner, so why had he needed another woman, kept secret from her.

Southwark Central drew closer. She prepared to move to the slower bands. It would not do to stumble. The rolling walkways were remarkable things but they didn't stop for anyone, so a stumble meant a lot more than a skinned knee, you could be dragged along for metres and involving others in your collapse was a social gaff of prodigious proportions. She carefully calculated the speeds before stepping to the right and dismounting.

The net gave her directions to the postcode and she confirmed with a short text that she had arrived in Southwark and would meet the woman as agreed.

The café was one of a large chain, bland coffee, Chinese tourists flocking at the bar. She scanned the other clients and identified the woman. Longish untidy mousy hair, not like her blond tight cut. A short plump woman with indeterminate face, cheekbones hidden in rolls of flesh, bags under the sleep-deprived eyes, red still from grief Isar suspected; she was probably unaware of the full terms of the will, for what she is about to receive I hope she is truly thankful.

'Joan is it?' She asked the question out of politeness; she knew the answer.

'Yes, you're Isar, aren't you? I've seen your picture on the Holos.'

'I ought to say "nice to meet you" but as my registered partner's lover I think we can dispense with the niceties.'

The woman began to fill up again. The eyes already swollen and bloodshot became thoroughly overcome with grief and she sobbed into a used tissue. Isar dipped into her pocket and produced a laundered natural fabric handkerchief which she passed over. She waited a moment or two while Joan tried to collect herself. A servo droid came to the table and Isar ordered for them both, high caffeine skinny soy lattes. The machine spluttered a moment then passed them the two drinks and moved on to the next table. A part of Isar's mind felt the disappearance of a few credits.

'He was such a lovely man. Warm, approachable, his artwork was so penetrating. We met at Art School you know.' Isar knew. 'Here in London, twenty five … no, thirty years ago. We had a thing going for a while, intense, you know?' Isar knew. 'But then he had his vision of where he wanted his career to go and the world he moved into … I just couldn't fit into that. We split up. Years later a random hit on the net and we emailed a bit, caught up with each other while you were filming somewhere and somehow the passion was still there.' Passion, what did she know of passion? Isar had passion hardwired into her DNA, she could make herself flare up with an intensity you would not believe. Passion from this mouse?

'He made me feel alive. And I gave him something you could not, with all your beauty, your perfection. I gave him love, warmth, softness. He could trust me. I was always there for him. Always.' It was a good scene, part of Isar reflected, she played it well, raised her head up at exactly the right moment to catch the light. Some mood lighting would have helped, perhaps less disturbance from other customers in the background; she would have spoken to the soundman.

'I haven't come here for recriminations. What went on between you and Erich was your business. I have only come to give you these, he wanted you to have them. I have no use for them anyway. The keys to the studio in St Tropez. I never go; an hour on the shuttle is just too long. He painted there a lot and most of it is beyond me. The pictures in the studio are yours, the royalties on the film rights are mine. That's all yours.' She placed a packet of legal documents on the table and his watch. 'I didn't get this though. He specifically mentioned this.' She held out the bag. Joan looked into it suspiciously then eagerly pulled out the contents. A faded worn blue dressing gown.

'Why in the world he wanted you to have this I'll never know.'

Joan had buried her face in the blue fabric, was smelling Erich with an intensity that was quite shocking in a public place.

'Oh thank you, Erich, thank you.' She was smiling even though tears were flowing down her cheeks.

'If you could sign this to say I have given you these items then the lawyers will deal with everything else for me.' Isar held out a pen and Joan added her name and the date. Isar sat back, surprisingly relieved to have got over that hurdle.

'Well, I suspect we won't meet again, so I'll say goodbye.'

Joan looked up with her brown, doughy cow's eyes. 'He loved me, didn't he? He really loved me.'

'I suppose so. You can think that. If it helps.'

'It helps.'

Much as she hated to let someone in this situation get the last word she couldn't think of anything else to say so she rose to her full height and held out a pale, perfectly manicured hand. There was a silent handshake between the two women and an almost insignificant nod and Isar turned and left the café.

The route back to Westminster Skies was uneventful and Isar passed it reviewing her future; she was an independent rich woman; the world was available to her and she could do anything she chose. Reaching the elevator to the penthouse she paused for a second for the security system to recognise her internal transponder, then rode the private lift to the top floor. The ride was always exhilarating; London's chimneys rapidly dwindled to sweeping views up the Thames and towards tonight's glorious sunset. She thought of Wordsworth's poem and downloaded the text. Words, rhythms, images she enjoyed. Reaching the flat she first visited the bathroom. Although she had little use for chemical fuel the organic constituents of human food had some advantages. It nourished her very real skin, hair and selected tissues, organs grown especially for her use. There were waste products though to be rid of so she must sit. She pressed a hand upon the gleaming white tiles which slid back to reveal a set of electrodes, peeled the skin from the first knuckle of the first and third finger of her right hand and placed the hand inside. There was a rare moment of displacement as if, for a few seconds, she was not in this world, till the energy transfer process had taken place. Then she was back in control.

An Intelligent Self Aware Robot with all the rights of a human individual. She would be able to inherit as would a human wife. She reviewed the day and considered her emotions regarding Joan. Tomorrow, she decided, she would call service and have her memory of Joan deleted. It was too disconcerting. Disorientating. There were few advantages of having a positronic memory; this was one.

Then she would fully play the part of Erich's grieving widow, till a new role came along. There was of course plenty of time to wait. None of her kind had ever died.

92

The cottage
Janet Wadsworth

The cottage was cradled on a hillside and looked south towards the sea, towards a triangle of blue between two round-topped bracken-crowned hills. The old stones of the cottage were painted a rich clotted cream colour. Its garden stepped up the hillside, setting down small lawns and rose beds and apple trees on each step. The vegetable garden, which produced more than might have been believed possible, was edged with clipped bay bushes. A totally delectable place to live, though the coast road traffic roared past the front gate and fuschia hedge, day and night, through the long summers.

An old couple lived there. They were well into their seventies. He tended the gardens and she made wine from the fruit they picked from the trees and the hedgerows. They both painted watercolours of the hills. The rooms in the cottage were rather like the gardens. They followed each other in friendly fashion up steps and along passages until from the kitchen a flight of stone steps led out from the smell and sound of bubbling wines into the windy scents of the garden full of birds. A long corridor upstairs led from a bathroom tacked on to the back of the cottage at the east, past doors to rooms which looked south towards the sea, to a big sprawl of a bedroom at the western end.

That bedroom was one place where the ghosts lived. The whole cottage whispered with ghosts, but the ones that dwelt in that bedroom were the only ones that made visitors too uneasy to walk the long corridor on their own.

It was altogether a haunted landscape. The round-topped hills were paved with flints, some chipped and sharpened by Stone-Age ancestors. The little boy picking up and play-running at a sister with a stone knife might have heard the infinitesimally faint warnings of a Stone-Age father to make him throw down the stone blade. The originals of the fossils which filled the blue lias mud of the sea cliffs might have shaken the ground round the cottage in their own day but now slept, waiting for searching fingers to dust off the mud of millennia so that they could be trophied by children and collect new millennium dust on a windowsill at home for a while. Their ghosts watched, gently amused by their own celebrity.

The lanes and fields and old farms surrounded by those round-topped hills were haunted. It was a rich, fertile soil in the valleys, so rich that most farmers preferred to use horses to plough their fields. Tractors didn't suit. They got bogged down in the heavy land and had to be dragged clear. The dead grandfathers and great grandfathers of the farmers approved of the horses. They looked on and nodded.

And long departed young lovers walked the lanes, private between the high hedges. Their ghosts still whispered to each other their dreams for a long dead future.

The ghosts in the cottage tolerated the old people and their family. When visitors asked, clearing their throats in slight embarrassment first, if … err … anyone had ever seen … err … a ghost in the corridor upstairs, the old lady would smile and say that people did sometimes think that they'd seen something. Why, she would say, one little great granddaughter of hers asked her where had the lady gone, the lady who'd been standing with her at the top of the stairs? But the old couple were at ease with their companions. They had a sense that the ghosts, people who had been happy in the cottage before their time, knew that the old couple respected the ancient stones and the gardens and the calm and simple character of the place; the ghosts knew also that the old couple would soon be joining them.

So all beings, past and present, lived in serenity in that cream-coloured cottage with its dark old furniture, the blackberry wine fermenting in the kitchen, and the newspaper open at the crossword, and books everywhere, and paintings waiting to be framed in the tiny workshop, and the sun warming the wooden chairs in the garden.

The old couple died with love and dignity. The ghosts mourned a very little and waited to see who would be the next owners. Their last human companions had lived in the cottage for so long that the ghosts had forgotten the possibility that people might disappoint them. They floated through the empty rooms and up the stairs, with the bad-tempered ghosts retreating to their sprawling western room, leaving comfortable nooks and presses for the others. There was some wordless consideration given to where the new ghosts might wish to rest, but in the fashion of ghosts such thoughts drifted greyly through the still air.

The place stayed empty for a long time. The plaster on the walls began to crumble. Damp began to seep through the roof, where ivy had dislodged some tiles. The vegetable garden was only a stony waste of weeds and the steps leading up to the gardens lost their clean-edged clarity.

Banging doors rattled the calm. Loud voices shouted, not soft country rumbles but town-ish blares and shrill responses. Jangling footfalls clattered up the stairs. Unsettling flusterings through the rooms, doors left open to bang, screwdrivers shoved into soft window frames, crude analyses of potential alterations: the ghosts were unhappy. The unhappiness grew disturbingly. Great groups of noisy people came with aggressive music and tools. The wooden fabric of the cottage was ripped away and replaced with plastic. Diggers tore up the stepped gardens. At night, in comparative silence, the ghosts moved with pain through their ugly, damaged home. Wordlessly they remembered the old man in his vegetable garden, forking the earth and treasuring the plants like his children. They remembered how the old lady would carry two mugs of tea and the paper up to the sheltered garden where the tall wooden chairs stood in the sun. They remembered respect.

Worse was coming. New, small, summer-let bedrooms were being made from the bedroom spaces. Shower rooms. A flashy kitchen. A walkway to the new lawn which had been dug out of the hillside.

One night there was a terrible fire.

The ghosts had congregated in the remains of the sprawling western bedroom and asked for help. The bad-tempered ghosts had offered advice and leadership. Easy. Burn the buggers out, they'd said.

The ghosts almost enjoyed the spectacle. They watched from the ruin of the vegetable garden, joining the ghost of the old man who regularly haunted there. They felt a kindred delight in movement and coiled with the flames as they soared and twirled.

No part of the home they had loved was burning.

The terrible fire slowed development for a while, but it only meant more noise and pain for the suffering ghosts.

So the fire recurred two months later. By this time reconstruction of the holiday cottage had been almost completed. Luckily the insurers were hand-shakers with the developers and fierce overtime finished the project ready for the summer season.

The ghosts understood that they had to develop new skills. Their home had been changed beyond recognition. Now they had all to learn to revise their ghostliness upon the advice of the west bedroom leaders.

The holiday company couldn't understand why bookings for the cottage failed to live up to their original high expectations. Many people cancelled their weeks and fortnights after a single night in the cottage, and the agents found that they were coping with demands for return of money paid as the cottage failed to live up to the description in the brochure.

'See there,' a woman would say, pointing to words in the brochure: 'Calm. Tranquil. Peaceful. Nonsense! Not one of us could sleep in that horrible place. There were weird noises all the time. Frightening noises. The children will have nightmares for months. And the cold. It was so cold. None of us could get warm, even with all the heaters on full blast. But worst of all was the filth. How could you think to let a place with slimy stuff all over the walls and in the toilets and on the washbasins and even on the sheets? Disgusting. No. We want our money back.'

It took the ghosts two years to regain their home. And what is two years in eternity?

The cottage gradually slid into easy disrepair. The roof tiles were tilted further by the ivy, so that the rain seeped everywhere and all the plastic flooring buckled, making neat homes for mice and small animals. The flashy kitchen soon lost any gloss and plants moved in to take over. Those partitions which had split the rooms were cheap fibreboard so that damp and rabbits ate holes in them. The old stones of the walls sank comfortably a little. Traces of the clotted cream coloured paint still clung to a few places, and sometimes the ghosts of the old man and old woman thought, as they looked down from their favourite sun-trap corner under a moss-grown wall, that the cottage looked hardly any different from when they had first moved into it. Over a lifetime ago.

Anne-Marie Vincent – Joff Rees

Exploring our Jurassic Coast
Anne Clegg

One day I'll walk those cliffs
while they're still there,
before a deadly shimmering tsunami
washes them away,
or salty winds
scour them into oblivion

I'll pull out from under the bed
my musty canvas rucksack,
trace a path on an old
OS map, check out some cheap
B&Bs along the way

I'll write a note for the milkman,
phone a friend to cancel coffee,
water all my plants before
reminding my kind neighbour
where to find the hosepipe

one day I'll stand in dinosaur
footprints and as I stare across
the horizon, steadying my sketch-pad
against the seabird windblown
views, those stories
will re-write themselves
for another three-year-old.

Writers' Biographies

Jim Aldhouse After a lifetime teaching, I retired to Dorset. A keen guitar player and amateur dramatist, I intended keeping a low profile having moved to Chetnole; by the first Christmas I was playing the Wizard in the Wizard of Oz! A poem should be the distilled interpretation of a single emotion; my short story reflects some of my prejudices regarding an unemotional alien future: Art helps us live together, technology only helps us live apart.

Gail Aldwin I've been writing for 3 years and in that time I've had short stories and flash fiction published. I was placed in the Winchester Writers' Conference short story competition 2011. I have two manuscripts sitting in a drawer and am currently working on a third enitled *Mistrust,* which considers the friendship and rivalry between three urban mothers taking a holiday in Dorset. See http://gailaldwin. wordpress.com.

Frederick Rea Alexander After living in America for 7 years, I moved to Dorset in 2000 and now live in Broadstone. My passion is script writing for theatre, and the first production of a script of my own writing is being produced at Poole Grammar School (where I am attending my final year of Sixth Form). Having spent half my life in Dorset, it has become my home, inspiring and comforting me. The future seems to be a challenging place, but for me I can always return here, to the place where I grew up. I also enjoy cycling to West Moors along the Castleman Trailway at sunset.

Judy Bannon Born in Dorchester in 1956, I have lived in Dorset for most of my life. I am married with a 17-year-old son and a demanding terrier. For the past 2 years I have worked for the Dorset Blind Association, a charity that aims to improve the lives of visually impaired people in Dorset. I attempt creative writing in my spare time, always endeavouring to improve, my goal being to publish a novel.

Benjamin Blech I am a freelance journalist and writer, specialising in environmental issues, global energy solutions and all things South-East Asia. I was born in London but have always been a country spirit at heart, travelling the world from the outside looking in. My main home is in Lyme Regis and I draw huge inspiration from the Jurassic Coast, a wonderful part of the world I'm lucky to call home. See www. benjaminblech.wordpress.com.

Valerie Bridge I am presently Chair of the East Street Poets, Blandford Forum. I have previously directed the Wessex Poetry Festival, had many poems published in the reputable small presses and had poems shortlisted in various competitions. I have an MA in Creative Writing (Bath), and have edited several of the East Street Poets Anthologies.

Lesley Burt Born in Christchurch, I have lived here almost all my life. My poems have been published in various poetry magazines and in my first collection *Framed* *and Juxtaposed* (Searle Publishing 2008). I have also received commendations in competitions, and was especially pleased to receive the first prize for poetry in the Christchurch Writers Competition in 2009 and 2010.

Megan Cannon   I have lived in Dorchester for 50 years. I taught history in local schools for 30 years and have two children – born and still living in Dorset. I love the county too much to ever want to leave.

Andy Case   Born and bred in Dorset, I have lived on the same farm since 1949. I married a farmer's daughter in 1964 and Maureen and I have worked hard, manually, all our lives, appreciating the nature around us and the work we do here at Milton Abbas.

Anne Clegg   I have won a number of awards for poetry, including Second Prize for the First Thursday International Poetry Competition. My performance poem 'The F-word' was a runner up in the *Telegraph* and published on their website and I had a 60-word story published in the *Daily Telegraph's Book of Mini-Sagas*. I have had poems published in many editions of *SOUTH* poetry magazine and been a guest selector.

Bronwen Coe   I have painted for the last 30 years, more recently taking up photography. Poetry has also provided a platform in which to express the inner language which I have explored in paint and photography. Landscape has always been my inspiration. My passion is to explore the hidden and mystical qualities of nature held within the landscape, bringing into relationship both general, particular, material and symbolic subjects.

Frances Colville   I returned to Dorset in 2010, having spent the previous 25 years living and working in Europe. Now that I have more time to spare, I enjoy experimenting with various writing styles and formats, and hope one day to fulfil a long-term ambition to write a novel worth reading.

Timmy Crump   Timmy died in February 2012. For his biographical note he had written: 'Born in 1921, brought up in Hampshire and educated at Bedales School, my father was a teacher and lecturer in English Literature, Speech and Drama. After a busy 65 years as a professional classical musician and instrumental teacher, I studied poetry to take the creative place of music, inspired by living in Dorset.' Timmy was a professional oboist, known as Peter Graeme. Shortly before his death, he wrote this haiku: 'My mind is empty, body full of nothingness, I no longer mind.'

Robin Daglish   I'm a retired builder and member of Harbour Poets. I've been writing poetry and prose for nearly two decades and have had several poems published in magazines. I published a short collection *Rubies* which is on sale at Waterstones and local bookshops.

Geraldine Farrow   During the 22 years I have lived in Dorset I have visited Abbotsbury Swannery many times. Initially I took my children, then my children took me and now I take my grandchildren. I find it an endlessly fascinating area to visit.

Janet Gogerty I have been writing non-stop since joining a weekly writing group; my long-suffering husband provides financial and technical support. I have had poems published locally and a short story in a national glossy magazine. My first novel is long, with no genre, but plenty of story. My second, shorter novel is in progress and I continue to write many short stories, light and dark.

Jennifer Grierson I began writing short – very short – stories aged six, encouraged by my school-teacher mother. Love of writing has run through my life's patchwork of occupations ever since, as a mum, art psychotherapist, textile artist and storyteller. Retired, I'm exploring writing stories and poems. I was born in Bulawayo, loved living in Dorset as a child and happily returned in 2004.

Judy Hall I am a successful Mind-Body-Spirit author including the million-selling *Crystal Bibles* and an Egyptian time-slip novel *Torn Clouds*. A past life therapist, crystal worker and karmic astrologer for 40 years, to my surprise I recently appeared on the *Watkins Review* of the 100 most spiritually influential authors this century. I run creative writing, crystal and past life workshops in Dorset. See www.judyhall. co.uk.

Janet Hancock I have lived in Dorset for 20 years, belong to West Moors reading group and was part of the successful campaign to retain the library. I am a member of Wessex Christian Writers, review for the Historical Novel Society and have had short stories Highly Commended in competitions. I am working on a novel set in Russia and England in the early 20th century, which won the Novel competition at the 2011 Winchester Writers' Conference.

Margery Hookings I am a Somerset farmer's daughter but have lived in Dorset for 30 years. I've been a publican, local newspaper editor, journalist for Farm Radio and worked in senior communications roles for public sector organisations. I've written a book about Bridport, have an honours degree from the Open University and write a Google Blog of Note, The World from my Window, under the pen name Maddie Grigg. I'm passionate about Dorset, the countryside and the local community.

Paddy Hughes An RAF fast jet fighter pilot before illness struck with a rare form of disorientation, after 3 years with BBC TV Outside Broadcasts I became a freelance film writer and director. I have made over 600 documentaries, TV ads and corporate programmes, winning many prestigious UK and international awards. My large collection of poetry goes back to 1970 and is widely published.

Pam Kelly I have been writing poetry since early childhood and still have hundreds of poems written on paper serviettes, the backs of envelopes, loo paper, etc.; but it was a brush with death in 2002 that made me realise how important it was to me and since then I have been sharing my poetry with others. When I am not writing, I sing, dance and act with the local theatre group and teach World Dance and Philosophy for the U3A.

Audrey Lee I am now 70 and living in Worthing, Sussex (though not in a residential home). I write a lot. During the war I lived with my Auntie Dora in her house at 21 Grandville Road, Weymouth. My son lives in Bridport and I visit Dorset often. I really love the place. The story about the book found in the sand is quite true, as are all the memories cited.

Jeanette Lowe A teacher currently resident in London, I was born and grew up in Christchurch. My parents still live in Dorset, and my mother came from a long line of Hibbses, labourers who lived for centuries in Winfrith Newburgh. I often visit Dorset to catch up with friends and enjoy the humbling coastline. I have worked as a journalist, written stories for adults and children, and am currently working on a novel.

Phil Mullane Born in 1948 in Dovercourt, Essex, I grew up in Newbury. My love of poetry developed following a course run by the Arvon Foundation in the 1970s. I moved to Swanage in 1998 and have immersed myself in the history and natural environment of the region. My interests include music, spending time with family and friends and walking through the rich and varied landscapes of Dorset.

Julian Nangle I was born in 1947. I have been writing poetry since the age of 16 and have had a few poems published over the years. My lifetime career has been as an antiquarian bookseller; at one time I had a small chain of four bookshops in Dorset trading under the name Words Etcetera. As publisher I published the poetry of Ted Hughes, David Gascoyne, Kathleen Raine and others under the imprint of Words Press.

Lucy Nankivell Born in Bridport and growing up in West Bexington, I studied English at Reading and Leicester and taught in Greece and Germany. I now live in Ferndown with my husband, teaching English, working as a freelance copy editor and copywriter and writing occasional verse. My poem is about the contrast between the two Dorset landscapes I know best.

Antonia Nevill A Dorset resident for nearly 40 years, I taught in Further Education and am a former Senior Lecturer at Weymouth College. Since retiring, I have translated 17 non-fiction works by major French academics, and am currently a member of the Weymouth and Portland U3A Creative Writing Group. My interests are reading, wildlife, walking and swimming.

Patrick O'Neill I have lived and worked in Poole for the past 15 years and am employed as a Research Analyst with a local Independent Financial Advisory firm. I am currently working on a collection of short stories which I aim to have published within the next 2 years.

Nigel Palfrey My story is about my time spent amongst furze and includes a Dorset man, Humphrey Pearce, I knew when young. He and others freely gave their knowledge and taught me many skills and country crafts so that I too could pass that on to the future. Humphrey often said, 'Remember the past, for it links the present to the future', and as always is so often disregarded.

Maya Pieris   Since moving to Dorset in July 2010, I have been involved with local food as secretary of the Bridport Food Festival, as writer of a food column in the Eggardon and Colmers View parish magazine, and I run Four Seasons Preserves. I am one of the Bridport Story Traders, attend the Cattistock Poets (my first open mic performance poetry slam was at Bridport Arts Centre) and am involved in a local radio project.

Helen Pizzey   I live near Wareham and am Assistant Editor of *PURBECK!* magazine. I hold an MA in Creative Writing and have been anthologised and published in literary magazines both in the UK and US. My poetry has also been set for large-scale choral and orchestral works (including the opening of the new Derry Peace Bridge and a commemorative work for *RMS Titanic*) and my short fiction is published by Leaf Books.

Jennifer Stewkesbury   'A Portland Life' was written for my two children. I was encouraged to get it finished and printed when I met the Rosetta Life worker at Trimar, the Weldmar Hospicecare Trust's day hospice in Weymouth. It was an enjoyable journey back into memory.

Lilian Irene Thomas (nee Lydford)   The late Lilian Thomas died in October 2011. For her biographical note she had written: 'I was born in 1925 at Sturminster Newton and lived at the Taylors and Outfitters, Market Place. I worked in the local Co-op as a grocery assistant, cashier and bookkeeper. I married in 1952 and moved away from Sturminster due to my husband's work. I have two brothers, with family still residing in the town.'

Janet Wadsworth   I have had a pretty full life, with three children, five grandchildren and now that I'm retired from teaching, examining and boat building (narrow boats) I enjoy my dogs, garden and writing. I also enjoy sharing these pleasures. Writing has been very satisfying. I've had thirty or so stories published, usually in small magazines. I've self-published a novel about brass bands, and sold the thousand copies which I had printed.

Karen Wright   I live and work in Bridport and love to explore Dorset's hidden countryside and coast. I am currently writing my first book, a children's adventure set in Abbotsbury.

Claire Wyburn   I have worked as a music and youth culture journalist and editor from 1991–2004, having lived in Glasgow, Edinburgh, Manchester and London. My favourite job of all time (except for writing fiction) was editor at Brixton's cutting-edge house music publication, *Wax*, in 1998. I went on to work for *Ministry* and *Club 18–30*. I have been awarded a Masters in Creative and Life Writing with Distinction from Goldsmiths College (University of London) and currently live in Boscombe with my 4-year-old son.

Poundbury Voices –
Editors' Biographies

This anthology was conceived, selected and compiled by Louisa Adjoa Parker, Maria Strani-Potts and Jim Potts.

Louisa Adjoa Parker Louisa has lived in the West Country since she was 13. Her poetry collection, *Salt-sweat and Tears,* was published by Cinnamon Press in 2007. She has also written books/exhibitions about the history of black and minority ethnic people in Dorset. Louisa has a Ghanaian father and white English mother, and started writing to talk about the racism she experienced living in mainly white areas all her life. Her writing has been described as 'honest' and 'raw'. Her work has been published in a range of anthologies and magazines, including the *Forward Prize* collection 2008, *Envoi* and *Wasafiri*. Louisa has co-ordinated Arts projects and run writing workshops in schools, prisons and the community. She has performed her work extensively across the South West. Louisa has recently worked on a project using images and stories to celebrate multi-ethnic Dorset. One of her poems was short-listed for the Bridport Prize 2010, and her (unpublished) novel was long-listed by the Mslexia Novel Competition 2011.

Maria Strani-Potts Maria was born in Corfu, Greece, and accompanied Jim on all his overseas postings. She has been an active supporter of cultural relations work around the world, and of efforts to promote British literature, the Arts, higher education and scientific exchange. Maria holds a degree in Social Science from London University. She has had a long relationship with Dorset (Durweston, Sherborne, Bridport, West Bay, Dorchester and Poundbury). Maria has published two books and a number of magazine articles. Her novel *The Cat of Portovecchio, Corfu Tales* has received consistently excellent reviews, and the Greek translation (Kedros, 2011) is enjoying much success in Greece. Maria has also published an allegorical novella in Greek (*To Poulima tis Panoreas*) about the environment; an abridged English version was published in *Island* magazine. Maria had the original idea that led to the *Dorset Voices* project. She is committed to Dorset and to the discovery, promotion and showcasing of new talent.

James Potts, OBE, MA (Oxon)   Jim served with the British Council for 35 years, in Ethiopia, Kenya, Greece, Czechoslovakia, the UK, Australia and Sweden. Cultural relations campaigns included *new*IMAGES, with Australia; *Scotland in Sweden;* and *New Wales in New South Wales.* Jim initiated the book and touring exhibition *Literary Links* (between Australia and Britain) and the *British Year* (40 British writers, and Publishers' Association exhibition) at the Gothenburg International Book Fair. For nearly 10 years Jim was involved with film and TV production and training in Africa. He later edited the journal *Educational Broadcasting International,* and other journals. Jim was Director British Council Australia for 7 years and served 4 years in Sweden (Cultural Attaché and British Council Director), where he co-edited *Swedish Reflections,* an anthology of Swedish and British writing. Jim's latest book is *The Ionian Islands and Epirus, A Cultural History* (Signal Books, Oxford, and OUP, USA). Projects in preparation include books about Dorset and Czechoslovakia (where Jim was Cultural Attaché) as well as song-writing collaborations with the Italian composer Raul Scacchi.

***

All members of the editorial team, known as *Poundbury Voices,* hope to inspire people from a range of backgrounds to become interested in writing; that is why they took time out from their own writing and research and contributed to the funding and resourcing of the project, in cash and kind.

This lonely night

Louisa Adjoa Parker

Sometimes, before she knows it, lies come spilling out of her mouth like a swarm of angry bees. For Abeba, the line between what is truth and what is a lie is blurry round the edges. Tonight, she isn't quite sure whether what is running around her brain is real or invented. All she knows is that she has a pain deep, deep in her belly, and there is blood seeping between her legs where no blood has come for a long time.

She remembers the first time she saw the blood, in a country a long way from here. It was bright as a scarlet flower, staining her underwear. There was no adult she could tell; none of the kids would tell the nuns something as shameful as that. They'd find old clothes and rip them into rags to stuff in their greying knickers. If blood leaked onto the thin sheets in the night, they'd strip the bed and wash them before anyone could see.

Her memories of coming to this place and the life she had before are hazy, like a dream. The man with a pink face (who smiled nicely at her the first time he saw her) took her with him on a giant metal bird. She hadn't even heard of an aeroplane before they flew, and suddenly she found herself high, high in the sky, flying above white clouds like puffs of smoke. When she stayed with the man (who she now calls Dad) and the woman (who she now calls Mum) those first few days, she felt like a frightened wild bird that had flown into a house by mistake. She hid in corners, didn't understand a word they were saying. She didn't know what toilet paper was for.

She leans back against the white-washed wall outside the pub. She feels dizzy and closes her eyes for a minute, shutting out the sight of the pale gold sand a few feet away from her. She wants to lie on the sand, sink into it as if it were the softest mattress money could buy.

'All right, Abby?' a voice asks, close to her head, 'what's the matter with you, mate?'

Abeba opens her eyes again and sees Ben crouched over her, his long auburn dreadlocks brushing against her clothes.

'Ben!' she says, and lunges forward, wrapping her arms tightly around his neck. He smells of beer and weed and unwashed clothes. She is pleased to see someone she knows.

'I think I'm having a miscarried,' Abeba says quietly.

'You what, mate?' Ben asks. He can't hear her over the noise from the beer garden – people laughing and shouting and the music from the jukebox inside drifting out into the night mixing with cigarette smoke, swirling into the air.

She leans into his ear, brushes her lips against his ear lobe as she speaks. She is tempted to stick her tongue out and taste his skin.

'I think I'm having a miscarried.' As soon as the might-be-a-lie has come out of her lips she can't undo it. It is said. It is done. His face, already quite pale, drains of colour. Babies and bleeding and broken hearts are not his thing. Not his thing at all.

'We should get you to a hospital, Abs,' he says, looking around wildly for someone, preferably someone female who will understand babies and bleeding, to come and rescue him.

'It's OK. I'm OK,' Abeba says, looking at the floor and biting her top lip. She thinks she sounds brave. 'Could you just get me a drink? Cider and black.'

Ben shuffles off into the pub, shoelaces trailing behind him, pleased to be back on familiar territory again. Abeba's feet are cold on the concrete. She has bare feet, as usual. She is not sure when she started running around barefoot in this country. She knows that some of the locals will think that all Africans are savages, but she likes the bohemian feel of it. It goes with her style: long, tie-dyed dresses, her woolly black hair in tiny braids with different coloured beads on the end of each one. She likes the freedom of the hippy people she hangs around with; the hippy person she has moulded herself into being. She has become very good, over the years, at blending in with her surroundings. Even though here she stands out; a black face in a sea of white ones, she also manages to blend in – on a good day she can feel like part of the land itself.

Ben comes back with a drink in each hand, spilling drops of liquid over the top of each glass as he walks.

'Here you go, Abby,' he says, handing her the drink. 'Cheers.' They clink glasses together. It seems strange, to Abeba, to do this. What are they celebrating? And why, she thinks, not for the first time, can no one here say her proper name? It's not that difficult!

'Have you got a cigarette?' she asks him, one hand on her hips, her head tilted sideways. With the other hand she rubs her belly, long slow strokes going round and round. She smiles her cheeky, white-toothed smile; she knows this can get her what she wants. She has a dimple on her left cheek that winks at people when she smiles. Ben reaches into his pocket and pulls out a green tobacco pouch and cigarette papers with most of the cardboard ripped off. He rolls a cigarette and hands it to her, putting it between her lips. He tries to light it for her but the wind is too strong, blowing the flame from the lighter out each time it ignites. She takes the lighter and walks around the corner, behind the pile of deckchairs, cupping her hands around the cigarette until the end glows orange in the night.

'Cheers,' she says, sitting down again, thinking she doesn't feel at all cheery. She wonders if she'll ever really understand the English language, with expressions that make no sense. It's so easy to get things wrong and sound stupid. She hands the lighter back and sucks hard on the cigarette to keep it alight, breathes the smoke deep into her lungs before blowing it back out through rounded lips.

'You sure you don't need to see a doctor or anything?' Ben asks, looking worriedly over the top of his pint glass. He has beautiful eyes, Abeba thinks, in amongst all that facial hair and dreadlocks. They are an unusual shade of brown, almost golden, like a cat's. They'd had sex, once, when they were both really drunk, in the public toilets round the corner. She remembers the cold, hard toilet bowl pressing against her skin, and the smell of piss. The warmth of him. She remembers wishing afterwards that he thought of her as more than a mate.

'I just needed some fresh air,' Abeba explains, 'I'll go home in a bit and have a lied-down. Thanks, Ben.'

He squeezes her shoulder and ambles off into the pub, his khaki army jacket flapping behind him as he walks. He raises his arm to someone on the other side of the beer garden and Abeba is suddenly filled with loneliness so deep inside her she gasps. She knows she might just be having her period, even though it's weeks late. But she needs people around her, fluttering like moths around a light. She wants to fill the hole inside her with voices and company. She knows Ben will tell people about the lost baby; news spreads like wildfire in this town. You only need to tell one person something and, within a few minutes, everyone knows.

She wonders again if it is an actual baby that is coming out of her with the blood. She thinks she would like a baby; someone to love her. She imagines holding a tiny hand in hers. She likes the idea that she is losing someone, that she is grieving her lost child. This gives her something to hold on to. She knows about grief and loss and can hold on to it tightly, as though she was holding on to a rope that would save her from drowning.

Suddenly everyone she knows (or so it seems – there are so many of them) is outside the pub, jostling to be near the source of that night's gossip. For a moment she shines like a light. She arranges her features into that of someone in pain, which isn't hard as her stomach is killing her. She groans, and holds her belly, bends slightly at the waist.

'What's going on, Abs? Are you OK?' one of the girls asks her, her voice a high-pitched whine above the other noises of the night. She reaches out towards Abeba, tries to hold her arm.

'No. I'm not OK! I'm losing my baby!' Abeba shouts, and runs onto the beach, towards the sea. *Follow me, follow me,* she thinks, while shouting 'Leave me alone!' She imagines their stupid goldfish mouths opening and closing as she gets further and further away from them.

The sand is cool against the soles of her feet. She doesn't care if there is broken glass under the sand – let it cut her! Who cares about her, anyway? She didn't ask to come to this country. She didn't ask to be born and then abandoned like a bag of rubbish by the side of the road. At least at home, she thinks, there were people who looked like her; people with dark brown skin and soft woolly black hair. People with brown eyes like hers, faces like hers.

Here everyone looks washed-out; as if they have had the colour bleached from their skins. They are white in the winter and turn red in the sun before their skin gets browner. All the girls have long straight hair that flows like shiny rivers down their backs. They have small hips, most of them, apart from Nicola, who is short and round and looks like a cartoon character. Abeba is slim but has a big bum. She wears long baggy dresses to try to hide it.

Abeba runs into the sea. The waves make a shush-shush sound; this seems louder at night than during the day. She doesn't think anyone has followed her; she can't hear anyone behind her. The cold makes her gasp but she keeps walking, feeling the water and seaweed pull around her legs. She doesn't know what she's doing but half hopes someone will stop her. She hopes there are no creatures lurking in the dark water, waiting to bite her legs. She walks out in the blackness until the sea comes up to her waist. It is black and glitters in the night. The moon hangs like an almost-round white button in the sky. It looks as though it might drop into the sea.

She is bitterly cold, and shivers. She stops walking and stands still, looking up at the sky. She wonders if one of the stars she can see might be her mother, twinkling at her. She wants, more than anything, to see her mother's face, smiling kindly at her. She hopes her mother has forgiven her for being the one that killed her. She imagines, in one drunken moment, swimming in the cold water until she finds her way home, the way fish do. The home she can only remember in pieces of broken memory like a smashed plate.

Voices are calling her name from the beach. No one has come into the sea to save her, but Abeba doesn't blame them. It is freezing, after all. Maybe they do care about her, a bit. She turns round and walks slowly back through the water, tears spilling down her face, warming her skin for a few seconds before they turn cold.

Rehearsing 'I do'

Maria Strani-Potts

Heated discussions about last-minute changes to the following day's wedding service filled the church, *Le Temple de Saint Martin de Ré,* while some prayed silently for better weather. Rain was lashing the stained-glass windows. The bride-to-be had been confident that the island's weather would not let them down. Now her skirt was wet and muddy. White roses, intermixed with seaweed, alongside shells and pebbles, decorated the church. Josephine had demanded romantic perfection. Baskets with small, cream-coloured net bags filled with blue and white sugared almonds occupied the back pews as well as white silk bags containing rice.

One of the three female Huguenot churchwardens shouted in accented English, 'Please remember not to throw rice during the service. Kindly throw it afterwards, and only when everybody is outside the chapel. There are not many Protestant worshippers on the island; we can't afford a cleaning lady.'

Karin, from Sweden, wearing blue jeans and a T-shirt that failed to cover her navel, was holding baby Jacques.

Richard, the priest, had neatly cut red hair. He was tanned, well-built, thirty something. His sex appeal undermined his Anglican gravitas. He was a friend of the groom and had been imported for the occasion. Both had received the best education money could buy. They'd been to Oxford together but then the groom had gone on to make money. The priest hadn't needed it. He'd turned to God.

Everybody was trying to get things right. Karin, playing with the baby, pretended that the priest's sexy looks were of no importance. The organist and the singers practised their notes, and the groom's ex-girlfriend read a French poem.

'Let's practise the vows,' said the priest.

The bride was serene, the groom self-conscious, the priest, a man to die for.

'Do you, Josephine, take Richard …?'

'What?' exclaimed Alan.

'Sorry … *Alan* … a slip of the tongue,' said the priest.

The bridesmaids were mesmerised. Karin's eyes were dreamy, she must have been thinking of the Swedish archipelago.

Just when the priest was ready to say, '… and you, Alan, do you take this woman, Josephine, as your …' Jacques started screaming. Josephine turned her head and yelled, 'He's hungry.'

She ran over to Karin, drew out her right breast, grabbed the baby, and silenced his mouth with her nipple. She returned to the altar. The organist played a loud chord.

Josephine beckoned to the priest. Her hair, down to her shoulders, had the colour of French chestnuts. Her breast, white, with delicate blue veins, overflowing with milk, was pressing against Jacques' ruby face. Neither a Venetian nor a Florentine Madonna had ever looked more transcendentally divine, or a more delightful paragon of maternal virtue, than this motherly beauty. Richard lost his voice and his eyes popped out of his head.

'Please continue,' said Josephine. Richard coughed twice.

The Huguenots raised their eyebrows. The priest shifted his glance from Josephine's breast to his Holy Book. The groom stretched out his arm. He gently pulled Josephine's blouse over Jacques' head and said: 'Let's continue'. Richard repeated: 'You, Josephine, do you take ….'

Quiet as a lamb, Jacques fell asleep. Josephine passed him back to Karin. Laughter broke out and Richard whispered in a deep husky voice, 'Perhaps a babysitter could take care of the baby tomorrow?'

The Gap
Jim Potts

John read the aluminium sign carefully before climbing over the fence to stand on a small natural platform, a rock-ledge overlooking the sheer drop into the wild ocean and the wave-beaten rocks below:

> Lifeline Counselling 131 114
> Salvo Crisis Line 9331 2000

Two choices! For over six months he had been intensely aware that about two thousand people commit suicide each year in Australia, around twenty of them choosing to leap to their deaths from The Gap. Perhaps one or two had been pushed or thrown.

For several weeks he had been coming for walks here, contemplating the metre-high fence, with its three easily climbed timber struts, and the heavy-duty chicken wire covering the gaps between them. Apart from the fencing, it reminded him of some stretches of the Dorset Coastal Path. He still missed Dorset, the English county where he'd grown up. He'd emigrated to Australia when he was twenty-four, but only recently had he begun to regret it. He felt trapped. He couldn't afford to go home. He'd burned all his bridges.

He'd often read the small, discreet, easily missed aluminium sign tacked to the top wooden crossbar here at The Gap. He'd heard talk of the local council plans to install closed circuit TV, free emergency telephones and a much higher fence, impossible to scale.

The Gap, Sydney's favourite suicide spot, on the way to the South Head of Port Jackson, belongs to the wealthy, well-groomed suburb of Watson's Bay. John had always loved coming here, to this ocean cliff and coastal walk with its dramatic views out over the ocean, and of the annual Sydney-to-Hobart race, as the yachts come out of the Heads and start heading south towards Tasmania.

He loved the old colonial architecture and restored weatherboard fishermen's cottages with their tin roofs (now millionaires' homes and weekenders) at Watson's Bay, where he'd often go to have a cold beer or to eat fish and chips. He would sometimes sit under a tree and watch the firework displays in Sydney Harbour. He liked seeing them at a distance, away from the crowds.

He used to enjoy swimming at Camp Cove, which was netted, and where he felt safe from shark attacks. He didn't like taking unnecessary risks! He really loved the coastal walk to South Head, which lead past the secluded, mostly male, nudist beach of Lady Bay, to Hornby Lighthouse. He was sometimes tempted to join the Lady Bay swimmers, especially on his way back, when he got a good view of the beach, and of the naturalists sunbathing on the rocks or just standing there on the sand, exposing themselves to the curious scrutiny of all the passers-by.

John thought about writing a last text message. But then he decided he would dial the first number; he didn't fancy a crisis support conversation with a suicide-prevention volunteer from the Salvation Army. He had nothing to live for, anyway. He didn't need a lecture about Hope. 'Hope saves lives,' they say. John had no hope. There'd been a huge gap in his own life, since his wife had walked out on him after they'd spent six years painstakingly restoring their dream house near Bowral, in the Southern Highlands of New South Wales. She'd become bored with the endless DIY and his collecting mania, his fussiness about antique furniture and interior decoration: one room per year, for six years! She'd needed another type of DIY, which he was always too tired to provide. He was more interested in watching cricket on television. He'd played himself when he was younger; although a good bowler, he'd hero-worshipped great batsmen and had always fancied himself as another Donald Bradman.

Now that the house was finished, it no longer had any meaning for him. He'd done it all for her. He was about to dial the 24-hour Lifeline counselling number, when he realised that his mobile phone battery was dead. Only one solution! He summoned up all his strength and hurled his mobile phone into the sea. It smashed to pieces on the rocks below. He wouldn't need it any more; but watching the impact made him shudder. It wasn't so much the flying bits of shattered plastic, so much as the loss of all the stored telephone numbers of his friends and loved ones which had hurtled into the void, into the surf to drown, without a chance to save themselves, or him. He looked back at Macquarie Lighthouse.

He'd researched and staked out his suicide spot quite carefully. It gave him some comfort to know the local history of the place as he was soon going to become part of that history himself. It was more likely that he would become a simple statistic, one more forgotten person who contributed to The Gap's one per cent average of Australia's annual national suicide figures.

He thought of the shipwrecks that had occurred near this spot since the arrival of the First Fleet. It suddenly occurred to him that perhaps he should have volunteered to become a part-time coastguard, even if they no longer needed lighthouse-keepers like Robert Watson; Watson (after whom Watson's Bay had been named) was the first superintendent of Macquarie Lighthouse.

Perhaps it was not too late for John to save some lives or to offer hope to sailors lost in storms! The sailors wouldn't be slow to express their gratitude. He could sell his house and move to the Eastern Suburbs. Could he even raise the wherewithal to return to England, to his beloved Dorset? What kind of work could he find there, even if he managed to get his act together?

He lit a cigarette and climbed very deliberately back over the fence, feeling in his pocket out of habit, as if for the ghost presence of his mobile phone. He found instead a tube of high-factor sunscreen, and applied some slowly to his lips and nose. He promised himself he would come back soon, and perhaps even work up the courage to descend the stone steps to the beach at Lady Bay, to find some new mates, to celebrate Australia Day his *own* way.

Dorset could wait, like it had always waited. West Bay wasn't Watson's Bay, and the fish and chips weren't as good there, but the place held powerful childhood memories for him. It wasn't much of a harbour, even, but it was a *haven*. He started humming the tune he knew for an old song called 'Linden Lea' and recalled some of the words he'd once known so well:

'I be free to go abroad,
Or take again my homeward road ...'

William Barnes, the voice of Dorset

113

Useful Contacts

The following groups, businesses and individuals responded to our offer of a free mention in the book. The listing is designed as a potentially useful source of contacts for writers and photographers, not as a portal for individuals to advertise themselves per se. Inclusion does not constitute endorsement by the Editors or Roving Press.

Allegoric
Allegoric is a Dorset-based graphic design and illustration studio specialising in the quirky and unique. If you are looking to bring your design concept to life we can help, from logo design to brochures, from illustrated maps to art prints ... and more. Contact Yvonne Lee: tel 07837 729984 / 01202 853680, yvonne@allegoric.co.uk, www. allegoric.co.uk.

Black Dog Creative Writing, Lyme Regis
Writer and teacher Joanna Smith offers fiction and memoir writing courses, distance learning programmes, mentoring, proofreading and detailed critiques. Contact Joanna: 0782 4617453 / 01297 444624, joatlyme@googlemail.com.

Creeds the Printers, Bridport
Creeds, the family printers in Broadoak, understand first-time writers and are well used to helping novices through the hoops of pre-press, typesetting, scanning, corrections, design, print production, despatch and marketing. They're 'people people' as well as technical professionals. If you have a book inside you, have a chat with Marilyn or Harry: 01308 423411, office@creedsuk.com.

Domini Deane (cover design and illustration)
Domini Deane is a popular Dorset artist who has created the cover art and illustrations for *The Portland Chronicles* series by Carol Hunt, and *The Smugglers' Town Mystery* series by JA Ratcliffe. Domini's art has also been featured in several publications, including *ImagineFX* magazine, as well as numerous galleries, shows, greeting cards and prints. Contact: domini@dominideane.com, www.dominideane.com.

Hinton and Christchurch Library Writing Groups
The groups offer weekly homework titles and exercises, individual written comments and some social events. A small fee is payable. Meetings are held at Christchurch Library, Wednesdays 10–12 am, and Hinton Studio, Thursdays 2–4 pm. Contact Dr Cynthia Collins: 01425 274804.

Imagine Books, 23 St Alban Street, Weymouth
Imagine Books is an independent book shop, specialising in local history. Our love of Dorset is reflected in our special relationship with local authors and artists. We hold book launches and signings, and offer local artists and photographers the chance to sell their work. Contact Ann: 01305 767965, www.imaginebookshops.com, or pop into the shop.

Mags4Dorset
Details of the mags4dorset annual writing competition are given in *4Dorset* and *Viewpoint Magazine* and online at www.mags4dorset. co.uk early each year. There are cash prizes in three categories: short story, poetry and article. Entry forms are available from mags@mags4dorset. co.uk or tel 01202 870270.

Monique Munroe (1stWrites)
Monique Munroe has been running 1stWrites since 2006. Drawing on her own writing experience, Monique facilitates writing workshops in the Poole area. These include short story courses, short creative writing sessions and a short story improvers group. They are ideal for beginners or for writers who just simply want to write with others. See www.1stwrites.co.uk.

Moonrakers Writers' Circle/Workshop
All-day workshops are held monthly in Corfe Mullen covering all aspects of writing, including structuring, presentation, characterisation and dialogue. Contact Veronica Wiltshire: 01202 696436, wiltshireron@btinternet.com.

Shaftesbury Arts Centre Poetry Group
Meetings are held monthly on the 4th Thursday of the month at 7.30 pm in the Proctor Room at Shaftesbury Arts Centre. The group welcomes poets who wish to improve their work in a critical but friendly and supportive group setting. Contact Pam Kelly: 01747 850789, www.shaftesburyartscentre.org.uk.

West Mead Creative
West Mead Creative can help you promote your work and services. They have helped artists and writers across the south west. Contact: 01308 423360, www.westmeadcreative.org.uk.

Yeovil Community Arts Association (YCAA)
The YCAA is dedicated to raising funds to support the cultural needs of the community. It organises the Yeovil Literary Prize, an annual international writing competition with significant prizes (www.yeovilprize.co.uk). There is also the Yeovil Creative Writing Circle which meets fortnightly on a Thursday at 7.30 pm in the Johnson Studio at the Octagon Theatre. Contact: Lin Bevan 01935 411564, www.yeovilarts.com.

Publisher's Note

Roving Press was delighted to be involved in this unique project from the outset. When asked to help put together a Dorset anthology, we had no idea how much enthusiasm and support the project would generate. Supportive comments from people embracing it confirmed the belief that there was a need for such a book – an opportunity for new and established writers and photographers to have their work published in something long-lasting – a locally produced and marketed book (Roving Press's speciality). The project also gained the support of Creative Dorset, for which we are most grateful.

As with any line of publishing, someone has to make a decision on content. In this case, the Editorial Team (three independent professional writers) carefully selected what they felt were the best submissions. Each of the three editors is experienced in different ways and all are published writers and have significant, wide-ranging experience in supporting and promoting literature and the arts.

The project would have been unworkable had we not imposed certain limitations; this included asking for submissions in electronic format for ease of processing, and requesting a small fee with each piece of work. This was to ensure that people did not send in their entire collection of writing or photography, but focused on their very best work. In return we hope that by providing a free copy of the book to everyone who participated, people would feel part of the project, regardless of whether their submission(s) were selected. We also stipulated that at least half the material selected should have direct relevance or connection to Dorset in terms of setting or inspiration, in order that the final book reflected our county.

We hope this original collection of prose, poetry and photography will inspire others and be seen as a great collective effort, something to be proud of.

Roving
Press